Something has been happening lately that has become increasingly upsetting and hard to ignore – people we care about are hurting, and turning to suicide to end their pain. I think the phenomenon is not new, but the visibility of it is, and the time to support our fellow men is long-overdue. And when it comes to support, men often shy away from speaking up or admitting the need for help. But in each others' stories, we find solace. We find help. We find hope. And we find a way to raise our hand when we wouldn't before. Guts, Grit & The Grind is that source of solace, help and hope we so desperately as men and as a society. I'm so thankful this important message is available.

--Bryan Falchuk, CPT BCS, Life Coach, Author, Speaker
Author of Do a Day and The 50 75 100 Solution: Build Better Relationships

Right book, right topic, right time!

Jeffrey Flack, CEO Jeffrey Flack, Inc.
Author, Certified executive Coach, Speaker, Trainer mentored by John Maxwell, Jim Britt, Bob Proctor & Sandy Gallagher.

Written for every man who has heard, "I wish you would talk to someone," and for the women who worry about and love them. Funny, poignant, and insightful... this is a book men will actually want to read, and it just may save their lives. No "therapy speak" here -- this book is written in "guy speak" so the medicine goes down nice and easy chuckling all the way. All kidding aside, I have no doubt this book will save lives. I'll be buying several copies for the men in my life and to put in my psychotherapy waiting room. I'm guessing every copy disappears.

Katherine Fabrizio M.A ,L.P.C. at DaughtersRising.info

Guts, Grit & The Grind

A MENtal Mechanics MANual:

Basic Mechanics

The Stories, Science, and Strategy to Help Men Build and Maintain a Life Worth Living

Sally Spencer-Thomas, Psy.D.

Sarah Gaer, MA

Frank King

Table of Contents

FOREWORD

Dr. Paul Quinnett

Most people know that men kill themselves roughly four times as often as women, and that 7 in 10 suicides in the US are by men. Adult white men in particular don't "age out" of suicide risk, but age into higher and higher risk[1]. These are our sons, brothers, uncles, fathers, grandfathers, battle buddies, co-workers, teammates, and the majority of our tax-paying workforce. From farming, fishing, and forestry to construction, mining, and medicine, men-at-work are killing themselves in droves.

The trouble is, no one is doing much about it.

That is, until this book came along.

I've spent most of my adult life trying to help men not kill themselves. So have the authors of this book.

For my side of the work, I've written articles, stories, book chapters, led seminars, and given lectures all over the world about men and suicide. The source code for my observations about men and suicide were men themselves; men I saw in my 30-year practice as a clinical psychologist. Most of these men were sent to me by other clinicians who were, frankly, too frightened to treat them themselves for fear they might take their own lives and leave their families to sue them for malpractice.

Me? I like to work with suicidal men. I specialized in them and saw hundreds.

Men who work hard in therapy, quit drinking or drugging, and stop doing stupid stuff are always grateful.

Men believe in paying it back and paying it forward. Do a man a favor and he says, "I owe you one." And he means it. Called "male reciprocity," men understand that when you accept something it is never free, but that a price must be paid; back to the giver, or to some-one else into the future. It's about paying one's debts. It's about the code of fair play and fair dealing. It's about honor. It's why mentored men mentor other men. Heartfelt reciprocity is the mark of manhood.

And it's about why the men you will meet in Guts, Grit & The Grind are willing to tell you their stories. They are paying it forward. On a grander scale, reciprocity is why the world works at all.

Only a few lucky men find their way into competent care. And it usually takes a life-threatening crisis to get them there. In general, men wait too long to get their testicles examined after they feel the first bumps. They wait too long to have their eyes examined, their teeth fixed, and their colons scoped. After a deep dive into heavy drinking or drugs, they wait too long to go to NA, AA, or rehab, and end up with brains whose neurotransmitters are so depleted that if you stuck a dipstick their ear and drew it out again, you'd have to blow the dust off the stick to read the "oil" level.

Just kidding. But the engine-to-brain metaphor is a good one, and one I have been using for decades with my male patients. As I joke with men, "If you took care of your car's engine like you're taking care of your brain, you'd better get used to walking or taking the bus."

Not reaching out for help has many causes, not the least of which is that when in extreme pain, our brains tell us, "Nothing can help, you're too far gone." It's called the "help-negation effect" and it's real, and it costs us all too dearly.

To get some men into treatment you have to bust their balls, or you have to threaten them, or those who love them have to drop a dime on them or drop the hammer to force the issue. "You either go to counseling with me or I'm leaving." "Clean up your act or you're fired." "If you're late one more Monday morning, you can pack your bags."

Do men wait too long to ask for help with suicidal thoughts?

Of course they do.

What man in his right mind would tell anyone they are thinking of killing themselves? Certainly no physician. Certainly no commercial airline pilot. A cop? A judge? A pastor? A farmer? Give me a break. Yet I have seen all these men, and not one of them got into my office prompted by following the thought: "Oh golly, I wonder if these thoughts of killing myself might have something to do with my mental health. Gee, I think I'll go see a psychologist."

Not one. All these men and many, many more were somehow "obligated" to see me. With one exception.

Tom was a suicidal businessman from a distant town. When asked why he had come to see me he said, "I saw you on television." Since I'm no actor, the only reason I'm on TV is because I give interviews about suicide. Like picking an expert mechanic for his ride, Tom brought his brain to me for diagnostics and repair, both of which were straightforward enough.

There's a reason men don't ask strangers for help. If you're a man, asking for help from a stranger is dangerous. Until proven otherwise, strangers are enemies, and in ancient times if you were a stranger in a strange land and other men caught you on their turf, they had a right to kill you on sight. This has been true forever, from the Bible to English Common Law to West Side Story, unwelcome male trespassers are subject to the death penalty. Or capture and torture, slavery, and sexual assault. Every man who must ask a stranger for help hears banjo music (from the film Deliverance), and we all know how that turned out.

The authors of this book have set about to change things in the world of men, and in how men see and think about themselves, not only in help-seeking, but help-accepting. Guys may not ask for help, but they will accept it if offered when needed, like when they are stuck in a ditch and need a push or a pull. Or in fight against the bad guys like in everything from the Seven Samurai to The Hobbit.

Men will also accept help if they know it won't kill them. The authors get this tough task done by being smarter than your average bears. They just went directly to men in recovery and asked them to tell other men how they not only survived their own personal shit-storm, but how they thrived in the aftermath.

To my knowledge, no other authors have done this before.

Humans learn best and fastest by imitation and by watching what happens to other people, especially bad things. It's why we all rubberneck car crashes. It's why we go to scary movies. It's why we need role models - both good and bad - so that we can give ourselves life lessons like, "Holy crap! Did you see what happened to him? I think I'll skip freestyle rock climbing."

In Guts, Grit & The Grind you will find life-saving stories about how men sank down and climbed up and out again. Delivered by real men with courage and integrity, this first-person storytelling changes lives, and for the better. Reading these first-person accounts will help suicidal men take a step back and say, "Hell, if he can make it, so can I!"

The day you read this introduction, another roughly 2000 blokes, men, guys, pinheads, and princes will kill themselves. That's a regiment of soldiers a day. Imagine that. Another 2,000 will die tomorrow. And another 2,000 the day after that, and on and on until we all do something about it.

To understand how men work you must lift the hood and poke around. You must understand traditional male values. You must understand "warrior psychology" – an emergent term that helps explain so much of what makes many men tick and why. You must understand team psychology, small group dynamics, and why men do best when on a mission of importance within a small band of like-minded other men who share the same vision, mission, and goal. And you must read about how tough it was for the men in this book to find their way forward in a world that chooses to ignore their reality.

Let's meet the warrior heroes of Guts, Grit & The Grind…

Paul Quinnett, Ph.D.

Founder of the QPR Institute

Past President of the American Association of Suicidology

Avid Fisherman

DEDICATIONS AND ACKNOWLEDGEMENTS

Sally Spencer-Thomas

I dedicate this book to my father, husband, sons, and nephew who have taught me much about men's resilience. I send everlasting love to my brother, Carson, who I know walks with me always.

Frank King

I dedicate this book to my lovely wife Wendy, who believes in me, even when I don't believe in myself. And to my darling little sister Jane, who is a joy and an inspiration. And finally, to my mother Dixie, the most courageous person I have ever known. She carried two to term that died shortly after birth, and somehow found the courage to try a third time and then a fourth. She is one of the reasons that I resist the urge to end my life. She was so brave and worked so hard to bring me (and my sweet little sister) here, in her memory, I must work at least as hard to remain here, until my appointed time comes. It's what Dixie would do.

Sarah Gaer

My life has been forever altered by the dozens and dozens of men, stoic and brave men, who have entrusted me with their stories of sorrow, pain, despair and even crisis. This book is dedicated to each and every one of them as it would not exist without them.

Acknowledgement

First and foremost, we would like to acknowledge our storytellers who boldly shared their experiences here so other men would know they were not alone.

We are also grateful for all of the early trailblazers and storytellers who have paved the way, showing that journeys of healing and recovery are happening, that transformation and even growth are possible.

PROLOGUE

Why the Car Metaphors?

Throughout the book we have woven in several metaphors relating car maintenance to men's mental health. We have found that linking these things helps men connect the dots — taking care of their mental health looks a lot like taking care of their automobile. As your Mental Mechanics, Sally, Frank, Sarah, and all our contributors believe that one of the keys to mental fitness is the same as the keys to keeping your vehicle running well: routine maintenance and when there's a problem, professional diagnostics. We hope that those who read the book will find under their own "hood" the maintenance and repairs that need to be done, and the tools with which to begin to do them.

As Mental Mechanics we help men pop open the hood on their emotional life and start a conversation. Contrary to popular belief, once men are asked and given permission to talk, the conversations can be as easy as talking to a car mechanic about something as ordinary and mundane as tuning an engine. Turns out a lot of men want to do the work on themselves, as they do on their vehicles, and are eager for the knowledge and the tools to do so.

Why Now?

As we are writing this, it seems like the world is going mad. We are amid an opioid crisis that is contributing to a concerning trend of "deaths of despair."[2] The mortality rates of men in their middle years are going up; almost all the deaths are attributable to suicide, overdose, and the consequences of substance use disorders. The researchers who coined this phrase dug into why this was happening and concluded that the trend is in response to the collapse of economic and social supports. In other words, men in their middle years are dying at higher rates because their expectations and hopes of living the American dream have been crushed.

They are like cars with many good miles left in them that all of a sudden find themselves up on blocks. They don't know why they've been taken off the road, and they feel incapable of getting back onto a road that leads forward to a place where they are valued again. Their motors are running, but their wheels are simply spinning.

During this same time that personal livelihoods and families are collapsing, we are experiencing one mass murder - with one gunman and four or more people killed - every day. Most never even reach public consciousness because we've become numb to them. Other mass killings dominate the headlines for weeks. Almost all these tragedies were perpetrated by white men in their middle years.

While these are more extreme examples of men in severe states of distress and violence, many other men are experiencing varying degrees of hopelessness, isolation, and crisis that significantly impact their quality of life. We know because we have experienced these as well.

Why Us? Meet the Mechanics

Sally Spencer-Thomas | www.SallySpencerThomas.com

Sally is a psychologist who had 16 years in the field of mental health before she faced a life-changing tragedy.

Her brother Carson was a 34-year old entrepreneur who by all external accounts was living an exceptional life. He had a beautiful family, hugely successful business, and many loving friends. Inside his head, however, Carson fought the demons of bipolar disorder and was often plagued with feelings of anxiety, self-doubt, and shame that ultimately proved fatal when he took his life on December 7th, 2004. In an acute grief state, Sally and many of Carson's other family and friends resolved to do bold, gap-filling work to prevent what happened to Carson from happening to others.

This passion led to new suicide prevention and mental health promotion initiatives aimed at helping men realize that they were not alone when facing depression, substance use disorders or other overwhelming life stressors.

The first initiative was a national effort to make suicide prevention a health and safety priority in our workplaces. Through collaborative partnerships and lots of trust building, many first responder, transportation, oil and gas, and construction communities - where the workforce is primarily men - are implementing total wellness programs that include many of the strategies outlined in this book.

The second initiative is a humorous, digital approach called "Man Therapy" (www.Man-Therapy.org), that draws men to the website portal with compelling media and encourages them to self-assess for depression, anxiety, anger, and substance use disorders. This program now has special modules for first responders, military/veterans, and primary care providers that use humor to bring down the barriers men may have to accepting advice and counsel. After all, laughter is the best medicine, and there is no co-pay.

Today Sally is a professional speaker and impact entrepreneur who uses her platforms to "elevate the conversation" and make resilience, mental health, and suicide prevention top health and safety priorities where we live, work, and learn. As a mother of three young men, her vision is that they continue to thrive in a world where men are proud of how they manage their emotional well-being and develop life-long skills of compassion for one another.

Sarah Gaer | www.SarahGaer.com

Shortly after accepting her first job in the mental health field at 20 years old, Sarah lost her third friend to suicide in a three-year period. She was so devastated by that loss that she had informed her new employer that she didn't think she would be able to work with youth in crisis. However, Sarah's mother encouraged her to try it, reminding her that she could always quit if it was too much (Thanks, MOM!).

A couple of decades later, Sarah has worked with many populations ranging in age from youth to the elderly, with challenges ranging from trauma to chronic mental illness, developmental disabilities, substance use related disorders and suicidality. She has worked in a wide variety of settings including residential treatment, outpatient, substance use treatment crisis, and outreach.

Sarah earned her Associates Degree at Holyoke Community College (1998) and her master's degree in Clinical Mental Health counseling at Antioch University New England (2009). She is honored to be part of the Riverside Trauma Center, a Program of Riverside Community Care, based in Needham, Massachusetts. In her role there, she has been providing trauma response, suicide prevention training, and trauma training to public safety and Massachusetts communities. Sarah was told that firefighters and police officers would never talk about their struggles. As she has learned - and you will find in these pages - when you give men permission to talk about their lives, they will.

Sarah has most recently published her first novel, "The Price," which chronicles the first four days following the suicide death of fictional character John Price, a beloved police officer, combat veteran, father, husband, son, and friend. The intention of this novel is to use storytelling to illustrate the ways in which suicide becomes an option and the lasting impact on survivors while also showing the reader where hope lies.

Frank King | www.TheMentalHealthComedian.com

Frank is a standup comedian and storyteller who was born into a family with the gift of humor and the curse of generational depression and suicide. His maternal grandmother took her own life after realizing her mental state was deteriorating and felt that "doctors have done all they could." Frank's mother found her.

That grandmother's sister, his great aunt took her life after being diagnosed with glaucoma and deciding that she didn't want to be a burden on anyone. Frank was 4 years old when he and his mother found her. According to Frank's mother, he "screamed for days." She said that she offered a deal to God, that she would give up 10 years of her life, if God would make it so Frank didn't remember any of this. He didn't until 2014 when, in an instant, whatever had walled that off in Frank's brain collapsed and the traumatic memory all came flooding back.

It was a blessing and a curse. A curse in that, up until that moment, he'd been blissfully unaware of his aunt's final moments and of his family history of generational depression and suicide. A blessing in that it explained the source of his major depressive disorder and chronic suicidality.

For as long as he could remember, suicide was always an option on the menu for him - for problems both large and small. He remembers one time when his car broke down and he had three thoughts unbidden: one, he could get it fixed, two, he could buy a new one, or three, he could just kill himself. That's chronic suicidality.

Shortly thereafter, he went from being a funny speaker, to being a speaker who is funny. He now had a story to tell, with not just ha-ha's, but also with lifesaving ah-ha's. He began doing something he'd been dreaming of since he took the stage as comedian: making a living and making a difference. He took those painful memories and presented an 18-minute TED-Talk-style event in Vancouver, BC. Today he shares his lived experience and mental health insights speaking on depression and suicide prevention for associations, corporations, and colleges everywhere.

He's doing what comedians since the time of the court jester were born to do: speak truth to power on behalf of the powerless. He speaks truth to the power of mental illness on behalf of people often powerless in its grip. He's combined his familial gift of humor and curse of mental illness to bring hope to the often hopeless.

How We Developed this Book Series

Through our work and life experiences, the creators of Guts, Grit & The Grind met many men along the way who, when their privacy was protected, told us the same thing: we need more resources for men. They also told us that they wanted to hear the stories of other men, men like themselves, who had gone through difficult life challenges, who had been brought to their knees by hopelessness, who had even considered suicide, and who now had embarked on a journey of recovery. They wanted to know there was a roadmap out of the darkness, a rope ladder that others had followed up out of the seemingly bottomless well of sadness and frustration, which would lead them back to the life of which they dreamed.

Sarah reached out to Sally with a burning idea to bring together inspiring stories of hope and practical tools to help men. Because of the connections we had made over the last decade through our work with men and suicide prevention, we knew we could reach out to dozens of men who had heroically fought suicide and other life hardships and who are incredible role models for healing.

We also knew we couldn't do this alone, so we reached out to Frank King. As he likes to say, Frank "puts the man into the MANual" - he also brings the humor. We believe that a little humor sprinkled into difficult conversations is necessary. He believes that where there is humor there is hope, where there is laughter there is life, and that nobody dies laughing.

Collectively we bore witness to hundreds of men's stories and were struck not only by the similar theme of the "hero's journey" in so many of those stories but also by the consistent initial belief by the storyteller that his pain was unique and that his suffering was weakness, a character flaw, or a moral failing.

This book has been both a labor of love and a massive collaboration. In our research and development phase, dozens of men took part in one-on-one interviews; over 100 participated in our surveys. When we asked for stories to include in this book, we were overwhelmed by the number of men who stepped forward and volunteered to share their testimonies for this project.

Findings from Our Market Research

Who did our guys want to hear from? The overwhelming majority wanted to hear stories from "everyday men they can relate to" but also over a third wanted to learn from "experts" in the field. So, we decided to make a book that blended the two perspectives.

From the survey, these were the top issues they wanted us to address in the book:

#1 Relationships and Marriage

#2 Depression/Anxiety or other Mental Health Conditions

#3 Stress

#4 Loneliness and Isolation

#5 Financial Pressure

#6 Boxers or Briefs (just kidding)

Everything within this book was created through the feedback of these men - from the cover, to the images, to the topics. We hope and believe that men of all ages and backgrounds will find courage, strength, relief, ideas, and laughter as they explore this MANual.

None of this would have happened without the courage and voices of our storytellers who responded to a simple call for submissions. We asked them to bare their souls to the world and shine a flashlight into the darkest corners of their existence in the hopes that their story could help others. They answered our call and their honesty, humility, strength, and courage inspired us even more. We hope that they will inspire you as well.

Why a "MENtal Mechanics MANual"?

While the creators of this manual would like to take personal credit for this creative approach to thinking about mental fitness, the reality is that this is what men we interviewed told us they wanted. They reported that they wanted something that they could pick up when they were struggling, look in the table of contents, find whatever they were facing, go to that topic and read about it, then put the book back on the top of the toilet tank until nature called again. They wanted a "manual" that they could use just like the one that comes with a new vehicle, that way, if another guy saw them reading it, they'd think car manual and that would be that. Hey, for a lot of guys, image is everything.

Why Storytelling is Our Focal Point

Humans have been healing and teaching through storytelling for as long as we've been on the planet. Our brains are hardwired to understand our experiences through story. Narrative Psychologists like Dr. Lewis Mehl-Madrona, author of the "Coyote Trilogy," have looked at the way indigenous people have used story to teach "lessons learned" and to build a sense of community. Dr. Mehl-Madrona explores the healing practices of Lakota, Cherokee, and

Cree traditions and how these practices converge with brain science. He and other researchers have come to understand that putting our experiences into a story structure - with a beginning, middle, and end, heroes and adversaries, trials and tribulations, and great reward for overcoming obstacles - help us impose structure on the chaos of our lives. When we organize our experiences in this way, we gain mastery over our own narratives and feel a better sense of self-empowerment, rather than just feeling like life is happening to us.

Stories also build community. When one person stands up and says, "This is me. This is how my life and others like mine have been systematically destroyed. This is how I see that change is possible." Others, who thought they were all alone, lean in and say, "Me too."

This process is how peer support comes together - informally, then formally - and then culture shifts. As Ivan Illich once said, "Neither revolution nor reformation can ultimately change a society, rather you must tell a more powerful tale, one so persuasive that it sweeps away the old myths and becomes the preferred story."

The Hero's Journey

We asked our storytellers to take us with them on their hero's journey. We needed them to set the stage for us of what life was like and what was lost in the downward spiral and darkest days. We wanted them to take us with them into the daunting darkness and the moment they knew something had to change. We encouraged them to share with us the guides who went with them on this trek, the incredible lessons recovery taught them, the obstacles they encountered, and finally, the great reward they now get to experience from their journey.

When we transform our wounds into sources of power, we change our narratives from that of victims to heroes. We make meaning out of our despair. The path we blazed through our own darkness becomes illuminated for others to follow.

Book Organization and Limitations

Our goals are to use the power of storytelling to create cultural change and inspire individual pathways toward recovery. While this book is primarily designed as a self-help manual, we also know that stories shared publicly shift attitudes and beliefs in our broader society. Our goal is that fathers, sons, brothers, friends, co-workers, and all men who find themselves overwhelmed can find their way back to a passion for living.

The Mental Mechanics Manual is organized into three sections:

- Preventive Maintenance: What do we need to do to protect ourselves from suffering? What bolsters our resilience? Scheduled preventive maintenance is scheduled for a reason: to head off problems before they emerge.

- Troubleshooting: How do we catch problems as they emerge and correct them before they become catastrophic? The Check Engine light comes on and we pay attention if we want to avoid costly repairs.

- Breakdown, Repair or Overhaul: What do we need to do when crisis strikes? Is the engine salvageable; can it be repaired, or does it need replacing? Obviously in the case of people, we believe it CAN be repaired! In fact, we have yet to perfect replacing our own 'engines' so not only CAN it be repaired, it MUST be repaired.

Throughout the book, you will see tips and suggestions like a car owner's manual. Whether it's Preventive Maintenance, Troubleshooting, or Breakdown, Repair and Overhaul, hopefully it will help you sort out what you see when you look under your hood. For your personal state of mind, we encourage you to try them out to see what works best for you. Is it something as simple as an oil change, or as complicated as an engine rebuild? Can you do any or all of this yourself, or do you need the services of a good mental mechanic?

This book is a primer, like the manual that comes with your car – it is not 100% inclusive of all topics or strategies, ethnic/racial, sexual orientation, gender expression, family composition, or industry. While we've tried to share a wide range of types of men, we were dependent on who responded to us and who completed their submissions. We know the perspectives are limited here, but we hope this sparks conversation in many new communities. We invite new perspectives. No automobile manual works with all makes and models but keeping most any vehicles running right - taking note of warning lights, odd sounds and smells, and solutions to most car problems large and small - is based on one simple principle: you take care of it, and it will take care of you; the same goes for mental health.

Many of our stories share important take-aways that would fit in other chapters' themes. We've distributed them in ways that highlight each chapter's major points. We hope you agree that the inspirational narratives bring the content alive in a way that data and theory alone cannot.

The "Ah-ha's" in the "HaHa's": Why Giggle Goggles Matter in Mental Health

Comedy is also inserted here because comedy is said to be "tragedy plus time." We can turn change into chuckles, loss into laughs, and pain into punchlines. Jokes are the painful truth, told funny.

Having a sense of humor is a sign of emotional well-being. Here are five ways humor helps our wellness:

- Stress-relief: When we laugh, we increase our endorphins and decrease our stress-related hormone cortisol. These responses help us relax.

- Connect: Humor pulls down social barriers and helps us overcome conflict.

- Distraction: Humor can take our mind off our problems. A good coping strategy when you are feeling blue is to put on your favorite stand-up comedian or funny movie.

- Perspective: When we can laugh at ourselves, we can often find the funny in our distress and put our woes into perspective.

- Positivity: Humor gives us positive feelings like hopefulness and amusement that can counteract dysphoric moods. There's a reason that it's called comic **relief**.

CHAPTER 1: WHAT DOES IT MEAN TO BE A MAN?

Why "Guts, Grit & The Grind"?

Through our one-on-one interviews with men who had faced everyday challenges or who had overcome massive hurdles, certain themes continuously arose. For us, the theme of "Guts, Grit & The Grind" exemplified some traditional values of masculinity that may help men's resilience but may also lead men to find themselves in a "double jeopardy" status. Men who demonstrate risk taking, stoicism, or aggression or who hold self-reliance in high value often also have more risk factors for suicide and are least likely to seek help on their own than other groups.

Contemporary ideas of masculinity have many more dimensions and challenge earlier ideas of what it means to be a man of honor and authenticity. Many of the ways we are re-thinking gender expression, sexual orientation, and gender roles help us expand our beliefs of what it means to "be a man." Guts, Grit & The Grind seeks to embrace the diversity of many expressions of manhood - both the old and the new. Without a doubt unhealthy, limiting, and toxic ideas about masculinity have conditioned many men to develop problematic schemas and scripts that lead to all forms of self-destruction and interpersonal violence[3].

What often gets left out of our contemporary conversations is the role that nature plays in understanding male behavior. Males of most mammal species are larger and more aggressive than females. Mammalian males are also more likely to die of risky and violent behaviors than females. From an evolutionary perspective, females of many species are more inclined to choose the stronger male as a mating partner. While the 21st century man is certainly not "most mammals," our civilization's evolution has far outpaced the human body's, and clearly more than a trace of this history remains among us.

Dr. Paul Quinnett also reminds us[4] evolution is not just about survival, it's also about reproduction. Not too long ago, men who found themselves "lost in another man's woods" were often killed, and males who couldn't defend and provide for their families often didn't have off-spring. From this perspective, it is unlikely that we will be successful in creating completely new concepts of masculinity that will stick for many - the wiring for some just goes too deep. That said, we do believe there is a place for appreciating the good qualities along a broad spectrum of masculine ideals.

When it comes to mental health and suicide prevention, Quinnett states, "So long as we keep repeating the phrase, 'encourage male help-seeking behavior' in our grant applications, public health marketing, and outreach efforts, suicidal men will just keep dying. Hoping men will become more like women is costing us the lives of our fathers, brothers, sons, uncles, and nephews."

The Epidemic of Loneliness in Men

For many men – in particular, white American men in the middle and older years, the demographic most at risk for suicide death - the scripts for masculinity have allowed for achievement and privilege but have also been deadly. Dr. Thomas Joiner shares in his book "Lonely at the Top"[5] that there is a high cost to men's success. According to the former US Surgeon General Dr. Vivek Murthy[6], loneliness is associated with a reduction in lifespan like that caused by smoking 15 cigarettes a day and even greater than that associated with obesity. Loneliness is also linked with a greater risk of dementia, cardiovascular disease, anxiety, and depression. And despite the incredible social connectivity many of us experience online, the rates of loneliness have doubled since the 1980s. Thanks to social media we are both the most connected and the least connected society in modern history.

The Stories We Tell about What it Means to Be a Man

In their incredible presentation entitled "Be a Man! Male Identity, Social Change in Contemporary America, and the Impact on Mental Health," presenters Brennan Gilbert and Robinder Bedi[7] stated that, "For many men (and perhaps all of us in the right situation), threats to masculinity are a threat to self."

Those of us who are trying to prevent suicide and promote mental health among diverse groups of men must seek to understand and respect the diverse and evolving forms of masculine self-identity and how these identities came to be. Shaming people for not being "politically correct" is not helpful and often shuts down conversations rather than elevating them.

Traditional scripts for men from a generation ago are being challenged today on all fronts. Just a couple of examples include:

- Over the last decade, the number of stay-at-home dads has doubled,[8] and paternity leave is considered increasingly important[9].

- Cross-gender friendships are more common and acceptable[10].

- Challenges to gender-binary frameworks and heterosexism are everywhere[11].

AND we would caution everyone to think about what is working within the traditional models that might be hard-wired for many, and difficult to change. In other words, how can we both expand contemporary ideas of strength, success, and providing for one's family while keeping what's honorable and functional within some of our more traditional models. If we embrace the diversity of many expressions of manhood, we will be a far more resilient species.

Referring back to the 1976 David & Brennan book "The 49 Percent Majority" - here are some ways we can expand our thinking on guts (risk-taking), grit (determination) and the grind (perseverance).

"No sissy stuff"

The idea behind this traditional value of masculinity is that to be a true man, one must not do things that have traditionally been thought to be feminine. For instance, if women are generally seen as skilled at expressing emotions and are more likely to seek mental health care when feeling unwell, then the "no sissy stuff" script tells men not to do this.

On one hand, we know that emotional intelligence is a critical part of overall intelligence, and the ability to effectively express emotions is essential for effective interpersonal communication.

On the other hand, within our current civilization, we also need certain people to effectively compartmentalize emotions to perform necessary functions that would not be possible if emotions were being fully felt - for example surgical, combat, and rescue functions.

We know that the ability to seek preventive care for many health issues is one of the main reasons women are outliving men by about seven years on average in the US.[12] If you don't believe us, take a long cruise sometime. There are so many older women, and so few older men, that the cruise lines regularly hire what they call "dance hosts" (and the rest of the ship's staff often call host-i-tutes), so the ladies will have someone to dance with.

Men's adherence to social scripts that support stoicism and emotional inexpressiveness are in opposition to "help-seeking,"[13] and yet many men would benefit from counseling and other forms of mental health treatment.

How do we bridge this gap? We understand it as a strength. For example, we have worked with many firefighters who have sought psychological services - fire fighters whose lives depend on decisiveness and emotional control - and they have reframed their experiences this way: "I didn't see it as seeking help. I saw it as learning new coping strategies, like a physical trainer for the mind."

"Be a big wheel"

For this traditional value men are conditioned to strive for achievement and success with a focus on beating the competition. For men, the world often seems like one giant version of "The Hunger Games." There are only so many resources to go around and it's a zero-sum game; if I lose, they win and vice versa. Again, striving for excellence is a good thing. The problem with this value, however, is that success often becomes the "single source identity." Men who buy into this script often identify primarily with what they do (e.g., "I am a provider." "I am a cop." "I am a CEO.") and are constantly striving to reach the "top."

The challenge becomes that the goalpost for achievement is an ever-moving target. In these circumstances, striving for success can become "the golden handcuffs" because men can begin to feel trapped when the achievement identity loses its connection with a far more important concept: purpose.

Work-related humiliation, failure - or even retirement - can lead men who subscribe to the "big wheel" script to feel like they've lost themselves. They can start to feel unneeded and adrift, a burden on others. A well-supported model of suicide risk identified by Dr.

Thomas Joiner[14] clearly links perceived burdensomeness to suicidality. Thus, our opportunity for the future is to help men find multiple pockets of purposefulness that can shift over the lifespan.

"Be a sturdy oak"

This traditional value tells men to be the one that people depend on, not the one who needs others. Self-reliance is a virtue in many circumstances. Having an ability to persevere through and innovate around problems is highly admirable. Nevertheless, the truth is that not all problems can be solved by oneself, and rugged individualism is lonely. Research supports the paradoxical finding that self-reliance increases risk for suicide.[15]

What gives us hope is a great emerging appreciation for the effectiveness of peer support among men. Over the past decade, we've seen a proliferation of formal and informal peer support programs in male-dominated communities - in construction, law enforcement, fire service, military, and more. Why have they been so popular? Again, Dr. Quinnett reminds us[16] that when men ask for help, they run the risk of appearing weak and incompetent but ACCEPTING help is another matter. When a man accepts help that is offered, he's still seen as strong, "but not quite strong enough to lift a car out of a ditch or drag whole elk back to hunting camp by himself." Accepting help is acceptable because it creates the opportunity for "repayment reciprocity," or the notion of "I've got your back and you've got mine."

"Give em hell"

Finally, this traditional value calls for men to act aggressively and display dominance, especially when threatened. In threatening situations, strong stances are often needed to establish boundaries and regain control. Thank goodness we have brave warriors and first responders who can protect the rest of us with these skills. Let us also not forget how many of us are inspired by the incredible accomplishments of some of our most aggressive athletes.

When this aggression isn't directed at a noble mission, however, men prone to aggression are more likely to perpetrate domestic violence, physical and sexual assault, and other criminal activity. On a lower level, the agitation and irritability related to this value can cause men to get in trouble rather than get support or empathy. Often what is behind this aggression is a male version of depression[17]. In our new diverse appreciation for masculinity, we can cultivate an awareness that emerging agitation may be a signal of depression or the experience of feeling threatened and intervene much earlier - in compassionate ways - before violence erupts.

Thus, in our effort to reclaim some of the benefits of the traditional ideal of masculinity and integrate them with contemporary ideas, we acknowledge that building resilience and finding ways to overcome hardship needs both Guts (courage to be vulnerable) and Grit (a commitment to recovery). We also acknowledge that sometimes life challenges are not about one or two major struggles but rather a collection of everyday challenges that can become too much, hence the Grind. The Grind, while sometimes less obvious, can do significant harm over time especially if we are not maintaining our mental fitness.

PREVENTATIVE MAINTENANCE

CHAPTER 2: PREVENTIVE MAINTENANCE

What is a mental machine? It's like nitromethane injection in a race car. Nitromethane is a dry-cleaning solvent and rocket fuel that adds get-up-and-go. It's there to give you that little temporary burst of extra horsepower when you need it most. Preventive maintenance practices help us build reservoirs of mental machine nitro, so we have the extra get-up-and-go to bounce back during hard times.

Think of the many things you can add to a car engine: glass pack mufflers for maximum flow through and power, a durable, trouble-free throttle body fuel injection system, and a Hurst Super Shifter. All these components get your car ready to go like gangbusters when the going gets tough.

Just like our high-performance cars, we need to keep our mental machine in shape, fully equipped, and finely tuned, so we are prepared when our strength is tested. And like a muscle car, we need to put it under a load. A car driven at high speed helps clean caked-on carbon off the valves and pistons. Take your mental machine out to the track for a spin. Read a good book, learn a new skill, teach someone else something, anything positive and life-affirming that will keep your mental muscle running well and ready to go.

A high-performance mental machine needs power, agility, and endurance. When it comes to the mental machine, our strength is developed by putting the pedal to the metal and facing psychological fears like fear of failure, fear of rejection and fear of humiliation. It's about being bold and down-shifting into the dangerous curves when we are afraid but not in any physical danger. Our flexibility and agility come from being adaptable and nimble and light on the track when life throws us s-curves. Our endurance comes from persisting for the things that matter most and believing that the long arc of our journey will reveal the gifts - and the checkered flag - if we keep driving in the right direction.

Just like high-performance cars need a pit crew to keep them lapping around the race-track, you need responsive and dependable supporters by your side to make sure you're firing on all cylinders. Assembling your pit crew is one of the most important preventive mainte-nance steps you can take, as we know social support is connected to all types of health and well-being outcomes[18] including:

- Buffering stress

- Better quality of life

- Better physical health and improved adjustment to physical symptoms

- Better emotional health and improved adjustment to emotional symptoms

- Better Homes and Gardens (kidding, of course)

- Greater self-actualization (i.e., the fulfillment of potential)

Not too shabby.

Maybe you're in a place in your life where you're isolated and can't think of anyone who could be in your pit crew. That's a pretty hard place to be. We hope this next exercise gets you thinking about the people in your life - maybe people you have not connected to in years

– who might be brought into this reciprocal support system where this is what you do; you look out for one another.

Quick Tips for Strengthening Your Mental Machine

Use Proper Fuel

You would never put diesel fuel in a gasoline-powered engine. Be aware of how you are fueling your body. Eat healthy, and in moderate amounts; don't overfill your tank. You would never add anything to your gas tank that would hurt the engine. Treat your mind and body the same way. If you smoke, consider quitting. Limit alcohol and avoid illegal drugs.

Use your moral compass/GPS

We all have a standard-issue moral GPS that's far more accurate than the one in your car. We get in trouble when we convince ourselves that it's okay to take a different way even as our moral GPS is screaming, "recalculating route," or, "make a U-turn." Sometimes we mute the voice in the dashboard by using substances or engaging in other high-risk behaviors. Sometimes we turn the radio up so we can't hear it and sometimes we just flat-out ignore it. Either way, we often get lost.

Top Off Fluids (brake fluid, transmission fluid, power steering fluid, coolant)

Think of your first car. Frank's was a tiny Honda Civic. The second year he had it, he was driving across the country and the mechanic told him he had "thrown a rod and broken the block." He asked Frank, "When was the last time you changed the oil?" Frank said, "Change the oil?! What's wrong with the oil that came in it?" Turns out you need to change it every

3000 miles, check it frequently, and top it off in the meantime. Ditto for all the car's fluids. Humans need to do the same. When we're depleted, we're no good to anyone. In other words, basic maintenance like staying hydrated, getting plenty of sleep, and taking helpful meds as directed helps us perform at our best.

Replace Air Filter

Did you know as important as it is to change the oil in your car, making sure the air filter is clean is even more important. Every bit of air through the intake that mixes with the fuel and gets fired by the spark plugs to make the car go comes through that filter. Hundreds of thousands of cubic feet of air during the lifetime of your vehicle. If the filter is dirty the air to the engine is dirty and the car's performance suffers; it will eventually break down. Similarly, for humans breath is the source of life. Leveraging the power of breath is a key to managing our sense of stress. If you exercise regularly, your lungs will get the most out of the air you breathe and your blood oxygen level will remain high, allowing you to work hard and think clearly. Learning paced breathing[19] will also help you control your distress and anxiety. Research supports mindfulness and meditation - often focused on breathing - as having an overall benefit for health, quality of life, and enhancing meaningful relationships with others, both in the short- and long-term[20].

Replace Windshield Wiper Blades and/or Headlamps

Have you ever gotten into your car on an icy morning and had no time to defrost or scrape the windshield and all the windows? You scrape one small spot, a porthole as it were, on the windshield, limiting your vision to one narrow view. You then pull out of the driveway, hoping for the best. Have you ever driven in the rain with wipers long past the time when they were effective trying to make out what's going on in front of you? Were you ever too busy to replace that burned-out headlight, until a cop pulls you over and gives you a "fix-it" ticket?

He didn't stop you for fun, or to make his ticket quota. He stopped you because driving when you can't see where you're going, or the potential dangers in the road ahead, is danger-ous for you and everyone around you.

How do we apply these lessons in our lives?

We need to widen our perspective on ourselves and our world and challenge our think-ing when it feels like everything is negative and always will be. Make sure you're seeing life clearly, as it is, not a narrow, distorted, or darkened view. Make sure your mind is focused and your vision is unobstructed so that you can see where you're going and what obstacles lie ahead. Also, when you use your memory as a rear-view mirror to see where you've been you can learn from it.

Regularly - weekly, if not more often - we must consciously pull out of our tunnel vision of the "conspiracy of busy-ness" to look forward and look back. Conspiracy of busy-ness happens when we are so distracted by non-important demands (e.g., things that grabs our attention and makes us feel like we are getting things done but it's really just another match on the dating app). We fill our days with these "things to do" and no longer have time to look ahead to build a strategy of what's really important to find a moment for self-care.

We can look back and give ourselves a pat on the back for the small and big wins we've accomplished on our hero's journey. Pat yourself on the back, literally! It will surprise you how good that feels. It's good-habit forming. One practical tip for "replacing the worn-out windshield wiper" is to learn self-affirmations. Self-affirmations are self-statements focused on self-worth in the present and future that emphasize core values and aspirations and give people a broader view of the self[21]. In the research lab[22], the reward areas of the brains of people engaging in self-affirmations light up when practicing them, and subsequently their behavior changes for the better. How do you practice creating this more expansive view for yourself? Flip your negative self-statements and write down the opposite: personal, positive, and present statements. Repeating them again and again can train your brain to aspire to what you want in your life[23].

Check and Rotate Tires

No matter how well the car runs, if it's up on blocks it's not going anywhere. If the tires are overinflated, it may cause a blowout. If they are not rotated and balanced, they will wear out faster. If the front end of the car is not aligned - regardless of pressure, rotation, and balance - the car's performance on the road will suffer. Managing balance and pressure is key to the preventive maintenance of your life. Look at your "Work/Life Balance" - or as a new concept for many, "Work/Life Integration"[24] - are you able to create synergy among all the things you value in your life? Or are you under too much pressure? Is your patience wearing thin, like the tread on an overused tire? Do your priorities need to be rotated and balanced? Look at how you spend your time and money; are these qualities of your life aligned with the man you want to be?

Maintaining Standard Safety Equipment

Seat Belts. Many of us are old enough to remember when cars didn't have seat belts. The only child restraint was our mother's arm that shot out in front of us as she slammed on the brakes. Seat belts changed all of that. You could have an accident, not be thrown through the windshield, and survive because you were prepared; you were "buckled up for safety," as they used to say in the seat belt public service TV commercials. A "Daily Self Care"[25] plan is something of a mental seat belt and shoulder harness. Many successful people have developed a morning routine that sets them up for resilience each day. If you hit something, or something hits you, you aren't thrown through the windshield. Specifically, within the 90 minutes of waking up, see if you can do most of this:

- [Fuel the body] Consume Something Healthy and Drink a Glass of Water (5 minutes)

- [Cognitive Wellness] Read a book or listen to a podcast (20-30 minutes)

- [Fitness] Cardio/Strength/Flexibility (30-40 minutes)

- [Spiritual] Meditate/Gratitude/Affirmation reflections (10 minutes)

- [Plan] Review Big Goals/Visions and Identify Weekly/Daily Priorities (5 minutes)

- Watch ESPN's Sport Center so you can speak intelligently at the water cooler at work about who won and who lost the day before (hey, it's a guy thing).

Airbags. When seat belt usage was extremely low, car safety experts sought to provide the occupants a soft cushioning and restraint during a crash event to prevent any impact or impact-caused injuries between the flailing occupant and the interior of the vehicle. The airbag provides an energy-absorbing surface between the vehicle's occupant and a steering wheel, instrument panel, structural body-frame pillars, headliner, and windshield/windscreen. If the seat belt is the Daily Self Care Plan, then the airbag is the Crisis Plan: deployed to soften the blow and mitigate mental damage in case of a major life crisis. It's always best to develop a Crisis Plan when you are not in crisis (just like you wouldn't want to try to install your airbag as your car is crashing - #toolittletoolate). More on effective Crisis Plans in our "Breakdown" chapter.

Regular tune-ups for our well-being are essential. Every year we should invest in learning more about psychological hardiness, mental health conditions, and suicide - before crisis strikes - as a part of the process. "Positive psychology" has taught us that daily practices of gratitude and kindness are powerful protective factors against hardship. When we learn to practice hope and optimism and engage our strengths in purposeful and meaningful endeavors in the world, it's like a superpower that deflects despair. Not every tactic here will work for every man. Try some, and if they make your journey a bit smoother, keep going; if not, readjust.

Meet the Mental Mechanics of Preventive Maintenance

In the upcoming chapters, you will hear the stories of men who have lived through life hardships and have found their way through. Imagine you are riding shotgun with them as you tool along and see how they've faced challenges similar to yours - how they handled the tight curves, rough road, and awful weather conditions. Buckle up! Here we go...

Rourke's Story — Letting Go of the Macho-Island Persona

I was brought up to understand a man is an island; emotions are for the weak, and power is the only measure of a man's accomplishments. Though I now recognize that gender is fluid and emotions are not reserved for one side or the other, it's no wonder I found myself drowning, desperately craving something deeper.

In the recovery world it's common (to the point of being passé) to hear, "I was in a room full of friends and felt alone." I felt that way for so long. Yet here I am, happy, joyous, and free, talking about what that feeling used to be like. Why? How was it possible to make such dramatic change? Reflecting on my path in recovery, I conclude there is no one answer - so much has played a part. However, I can say with certainty that though humans are complicated, the most underrated, consistent, and important part of my journey has been community and the connections therein.

Born into a family that took advantage of all that Colorado has to offer, I grew up with the standard benchmarks of sports a boy "should" have, but I was lucky that weekends were spent in the mountains. I was given a wonderful life full of love, fun, and support. Yet, by the time I was eight years old, I woke up every day with the deep, pervasive knowledge that I was flawed. Somehow, I'd "missed the mark." I wasn't smart. I had no idea what confidence was. I certainly wasn't strong. There was no way people would like me for who I really was. These messages played in my head every day for years, until I found something that fixed it all.

One night, two friends and I decided to raid the parents' liquor cabinet. It started with one hit of Bacardi Spiced Rum. One drink turned into two, two into four, four into... and so on. I remember feeling joy, comfort, acceptance. I could be whoever I wanted to be. I was popular, funny, and confident. Though that night ended as well as one might expect for a 12-year-old drinking rum, I knew I had found a solution to my problems. I followed that solution to the very edge of death, both through severe withdrawals and ultimately with a plan to kill myself. That childhood drinking memory matured into something of a heartbreaking yet hopeful allegory for addiction, as one of those three kids died a few years later, another was incarcerated at an early age, and one found recovery...

One month after my 21st birthday I was released from another stint at the hospital; this one the most severe. After two seizures, 6 months of auditory hallucinations and auras, I had tried another futile attempt at putting the liquor down. This particular attempt sent me into a full-blown withdrawal. I was no longer just hearing noises; I was seeing, hearing, and talking to things that weren't there. I couldn't use my hands, as they had curled up and wouldn't open. I was no longer able to stomach food. I knew, without a doubt, I was dying. It was then that my dear friend found me half-coherent and shaking. I asked to be taken to a priest to be given my last rites, but thankfully, at her better judgment, she took me to the hospital. I spent the next 4 days in the ICU. On the fourth day, I woke to the police, my parents, and the doctors telling me I was no longer welcome in Steamboat. The doctors informed me that, given the status of my liver, I had a year left (maybe two) if I continued drinking. With that knowledge in hand, I left and did the only logical thing I could do: drink.

Leaving Steamboat and moving back to my hometown, I was surrounded by family and childhood friends. They didn't like what I was doing to myself. They tried to love me, to help, all of them did, but I couldn't accept that the answer to all my problems was the very thing I had to give up. This ultimately led to getting kicked out of the house I grew up in. Homeless, I turned to the only remaining friend that would let me crash on his couch. It didn't take long before he realized the drunk mess he'd let in the house and tried to hide my booze. It was then, in what felt like abandonment from the last person willing to give me a chance, that I sat alone weighing the options: drink or kill myself.

To quit drinking wasn't up for consideration. It was drink or die. I don't know how long I sat there, but in that time I received phone calls from my family saying they loved me, friends wishing I'd accept help, and a wonderful counselor whose program I had attended. She told me that I was welcome back to the program any time and that I was cared for. In a moment, everything changed. The thought crossed my mind that maybe I could stop drinking. I might never be happy again, but at the very least I wouldn't have to live with the hurt I was putting my family through. I could just live... not happy, not drunk. I could not have possibly known the great life that was waiting for me, but sometimes we need to experience hopelessness to experience the amazing.

That was April 12, 2007. I told my counselor I'd get through the weekend as that was as far into the future as I could fathom, but I would be there Monday. When I arrived, she said something I will never forget. She said, "I don't know what happened to you, but something did." She was right. Compared to the kid that showed up before - sitting in the back of the room, hat down, two fingers up (you guess which ones) - that day I stood there desperate and ready for help.

Finally, willing to let go of my so-called "macho-island persona," I could admit that I was broken and willing to do whatever it took. That was where my journey really took off.

Over a decade later, I can't help but marvel at how fortunate I was. I credit that fortune for lighting the spark of the passions and life I have today. That same counselor told me to go to a recovery support group (for me it was 12-step, but that is not the rule for everyone as there are many options). There, I found a group of 10-15 young people who had anywhere from one to two years in recovery. These people were serious about their recovery, but also about having fun.

I walked in to that first meeting scared, trying to act tough. They welcomed me with open arms. They told stories about themselves that resonated because they were the same stories I had. I wasn't the only new addition; around that time 10-15 other young peo-ple equally desperate for a new life joined the group. The newbies banded together while we were being taught and welcomed in by those who came before us. Eventually the two groups became one unit, and we stuck together for years. Our lives became entwined as we would stay up late talking about recovery, struggles, life, or just making fun of each other and laughing until our stomachs hurt.

Of course, there were hard times for sure. Each of us would falter, but we did it together. When one of us fell, the rest picked us up. We challenged each other to grow and pushed each other to do things that were uncomfortable. No matter what, we did it together. Ten years later, of the 30 or so of that original group, nearly all of us are still in recovery and truly thriving. Though we're no longer together geographically, we still talk about how amazing and fortunate we are. Given the stories we generally hear about failed recovery, it's something of a miracle that the summer of 2007 brought a group of complete strangers together and created something so powerful. It's that experience that has driven me and others from that group to try and replicate a similar journey for others.

At a time of increasing understanding of how the brain works, its response to trauma, and clinical modalities, it's easy to overlook the importance community and connection plays in mental health, substance abuse, and overall quality of life. It's only natural to want to find a quick solution, an answer that is definable and quantifiable. Community is just too nebulous. I want to try to quantify our group of 30 random people coming together but, sadly, with too many variables it's impossible to define.

Can we learn to embrace this? When I reflect on my recovery, I cannot help but notice that the one constant through all my journey has been community. It was community that supported me in finding new life, continuing to foster a desire to grow, and continuing to help me become the man I want to be.

To create community for all, we must allow for all forms of recovery to flourish. There is no one right way. A person should be able to define their own recovery journey and find the community that best suits them. For eight years, I had the great privilege of working for Phoenix Multisport, a free sober active community that uses CrossFit, climbing, hiking, running, cycling, yoga and more, to foster human connection and total wellness as a way to "rebuild wounded bodies and spirits and restore hope." I have worked with advocacy groups that support All Recovery Meetings welcoming anyone who defines themselves as "in recovery." There are more Recovery Community Organizations starting all the time, and they need our support to grow. Community is further jeopardized in a society that increasingly relies on the absence of face-to-face interaction, short-term treatment, pseudo-connections via social media and internet reinforcing the island mentality. All of these are part of modern life, but without community, what are we left with? I truly believe community is the key to long term happiness.

Recovery is real, but we need to do more to educate society that the means through which we sustain recovery is through community. This is not to diminish the role clinical support, treatment, and coaching play, but we MUST acknowledge that as clinicians and providers we are limited in how often, how much, and how open our services can be.

In April 2017 I celebrated ten years in recovery. I am still an active member in multiple recovery pathways. Currently, I work in extended care treatment, which focuses on providing a holistic bridge to recovery. I have an incredible group of friends and family who show unending love. Shockingly, I am still hitched to my wonderful girlfriend of four years. I am truly in love — which I can say I never actually thought was possible. Having said all of this, I am not exempt from bad days. Seriously.

I struggle to balance my life and work because I want to do everything.

I struggle to accept that I am still enough just as I am.

I struggle to show up and continue to grow this wonderful relationship that I have.

I struggle, but that's ok. Such is life. Life can be hard. I'm still not the smartest, nor the most confident, and certainly not the strongest person out there, but because of the support I have I live a wonderfully good life. It is because of my community that though I may struggle at times, the struggle is vastly outweighed by the joy of what I have around me.

Doug's Story: The "Grit-full" Dad

How Gratitude Brought Me Back from Despair, and Closer to My Father, Son, and Myself

This story begins in the year 2007 when I had it all. The business I'd been building for seven years was peaking, and I brought in my highest income ever. Along with my wife and our son, I spent over three weeks traveling to four Hawaiian Islands. I was on top of my game and on top the world. In fact, when asked, "How are you doing, Doug?" my flippant response was usually, "If I were doing any better, I'd need a criminal defense lawyer."

Neither humility nor gratitude were on my radar in those heady times. But as we know, after 2007 came 2008; for me, however, it wasn't the financial crash, or that my business came crashing down with it, that really threw me into a tailspin. Rather, during June of that year I took on the care of my aging father, and suddenly it was like having a second child and a second job, neither of which I had planned for.

I'm a planner; in fact, in my work as a seminar leader, my most popular topic is teaching others how to plan and prioritize to gain greater balance in their own lives. When the call came, and I needed to step up and take care of my own dad, my world was rocked, my identity nearly shattered, and I felt confused about my own purpose, path, and place in life. I couldn't plan my days because my father might need me, and life became a foggy spiral of his medical visits and calls to insurance companies. I was physically, mentally, and emotionally spent, and had little time or energy to bolster myself or my business. "Who am I?" was the question constantly on my mind. "I don't know anymore" was most often the answer.

During the next three years I foundered, my psyche reduced to a fleeting memory of when confidence brimmed, and motivation inspired energy for life. Grasping for guidance, I reached out to guys and gurus. I pleaded with friends to support me, and I paid coaches to direct me. I was lost at the bottom of my own self-pity, and this lifelessness was a drain on my family that brought us all down and added tension to every interaction. Something had to change, and soon it did. And so begins the story of falling lower than ever before, and how gratitude (and guts, grit, and grind) returned me to the place of contentment I now enjoy.

Since becoming a father I have celebrated the many joys that role brings. As a long-time fan of the band the Grateful Dead, it was natural for me to adopt the moniker and persona of The Grateful Dad. In the process of branding myself, I began a radio show and blog under that name. And it occurred to me that the path out of my deep funk was to 'walk my talk,' and that, in fact, in spite of my tribulations and depression I truly had so much to be grateful for.

So I began the new year 2012 with a new gratitude journal, and made the commitment to be grateful every day and to note what it was I was thankful for. On my weekly radio show, in my blogs and speeches, I also recounted my gratitude and reflected on full-circle fatherhood, with stories of how I was caring for both my son and my father. It didn't take long before I saw benefits in every aspect of my life and work. It broke down a lot like this:

- Confidence & Motivation – The first steps toward feeling better about myself, and more ready to take on the world, were aided by support from friends, loved ones and great coaches. As a path upward, I suggest that everyone do all they can to surround themselves with folks who make you feel good and give good advice. Their advice will surely include keeping a gratitude journal.

- Recognition & Opportunity - Once my confidence rose, and with it my motivation, I became more focused, put gratitude front and center, and just put it out there into the world. Soon I was being invited to give talks, I was getting quoted in articles, and generally I began attracting positive people and great reactions to whatever I did. The more grateful I was, the more doors that opened for me, and I know that gratitude will make good things happen for you as well.

- Satisfaction & Productivity – As my year of living gratefully continued, and each day I noted my gratitude for both the mundane and the profound, the one-time and the ongoing things going right in my life, I not only became more satisfied on a daily basis, but also more productive. Realizing how much I have going for me helped me get more done and so more of the very things that I was celebrating. Try it and you too will find that gratitude actually grows more of what you want.

- Success & More Money – Here's the crazy thing: during that entire year focused on gratitude, I actually worked less and made more money. It's true. I took off every Monday for my radio show, which is unpaid, and had my highest annual income ever. Go figure? All I can point to is my investment in gratitude. Joy & Contentment – This is the most important and delightful reward from my year of living gratefully. Better than being recognized, or productive, or earning more, it's the sense of happiness and inner peace that is truly the best outcome of all. I need only recall how low I'd sunk, and that the path back up was paved with gratitude, and you can see why I am encouraging you to have a grateful day, every day.

So there you have it, one year, one simple act of daily gratitude, and so many fantastic rewards:

Confidence & Motivation

Recognition & Opportunity

Satisfaction & Productivity

Success & More Money

Contentment & More Joy

Are you ready to give it a try?

My path is not hard to follow, and so I suggest getting a gratitude journal. You can use any old notebook, purchase a designated journal (I found my first one on Amazon), or use an app or online portal to record your daily gratitude. Like so many things, just do it. Start or end each day by noting three to five things you're grateful for. They can be the same every day, or an expanding list of the many ways you find to celebrate the gifts we are all given. Stick with it and see the rewards multiply.

And now, a short epilogue to the story I started telling you above: Clearly 2012 was a particularly good year, due in no small measure to consistently and mindfully living gratefully. And as 2013 began, all those rewards really paid off when my father – who I'd been caring for over four years – took a turn for the worse.

As the year began, my dad seemed particularly withdrawn. Our visits were less engaged than usual. He'd lost the sense of humor that I'd always known, that had sustained him and marked his attitude in the nursing home for more than 20 months. In late January I was awakened by a call from a nurse there saying my father was in respiratory distress. By the time I got there, he was barely responsive. Within 48 hours he was in the emergency room, and then on to the ICU. From there it was hospice. A week after that first call, I was at his side, holding his hand and stroking his head as my father took his last breath. Through it all, I was sustained by my attitude of gratitude – for the man who gave me life, who took such loving care of me for so many years, and for the privilege of caring for my dad during his final four years.

Gratitude is what sustained me daily in the months leading up to my father's death, and it was gratitude that helped comfort me when he was gone. Just another reward for being grateful.

Whatever goals you have in life, whatever challenges you face – personally or professionally – gratitude is your greatest asset. Use it every day!

Joel's Story — First-time Father at 50

Flash back to 1998, I was living my American dream. I had a fantastic job as a sales consultant for a commercial printing company, earning nearly double what some of my friends were earning. My first wife and I were settling into our first home, we were driving new cars, and had just bought a timeshare condo in Orlando, FL. It felt like I was finally achieving the status necessary for me to feel accepted, even admired by my peers. The wounds of my childhood left me with a deep-seated sense of feeling burdensome and unlovable, and I felt I could overcome those feelings with materialistic possessions and money.

Then things started to change. I wasn't happy at home and hid it with excuses not to be at home. Golf, fishing trips, working late and all-too-frequently drinking with the fellas. This put tremendous strains on my marriage, and I started to resent my wife at that time. At work, I started chasing big dollar accounts, paying little attention to what I deemed less worthy clientele. It didn't take long for my sales to slip and to find myself on the hotseat. I started to blame people around me for the "bad" stuff that was beginning to happen. I became incredibly angry and bitter; inside I was freaking out...I didn't know what to do. I knew I couldn't ask for help because I was a burden and unlovable. These feelings were reinforced by what was happening in my life at that moment.

The anger and bitterness started to fuel my pride, to the point when I issued my employer an ultimatum which ultimately led to my resignation. I didn't get the job I thought I'd walk into and, after depleting the funds from a retirement account my (then) wife and I cashed in, I took a job as a laborer for a landscaping company and a waiter at a restaurant bar. I started drinking in excess and smoking pot, desperately seeking to be numb to the reality around me. By 2000, I was separated from my wife, then bankruptcy and divorce followed. I pulled up my roots in Cheyenne, Wyoming and moved to Denver. In 2005, I remarried an amazing woman and settled in.

She was working full-time and going to school while I was back in the printing business, this time as a shipping and warehouse manager. Food was now my drug of choice, and I had ballooned up to 377 lbs. I was in a mental funk, just going through the motions. Then one Monday in late 2009, I missed shipping a critical package, causing an unnecessary expense of hundreds of dollars; not a huge deal, but the upset jolted me out of my comfort zone and left me feeling less than worthless. I felt I was wasting my own life and the lives of those around me. In that moment I decided to end my life. A sense of calm, one I had never experienced, came over me, creating an almost euphoric state of being. On my drive home from work that evening I made my plan for how I was going to end my suffering.

Tuesday at lunch, I would ride the bike I brought to work (originally intended to use for cardio exercise over the noon hour) to a secluded spot along the Platte River trail and end my life. Monday evening, while my wife was getting ready for bed, I loaded my 9mm handgun and put it in my work backpack. Once at my desk the next morning, I drafted a letter apologizing to everyone I felt I had wronged, tucked it about half-way down my inbox, and I took off on my bicycle feeling as peaceful and resolved as I have ever felt.

Riding past Mile High Stadium, making the turn north where the path parallels Eltich Gardens, the water in the river seemed louder, making its presence known. Then feelings from my childhood, when I got my first bike, came back - not just bits and pieces, but like a flash-flood. For the first time in a LONG time I felt alive! My heart was pounding as I rolled my 377-pound frame into Confluence Park. I stopped and took in what I was seeing: the Platte River and Cherry Creek converging, the Rocky Mountains towering above the horizon beyond the cityscape.

The will to live had been breathed back into my soul.

That ride along the river led me to take charge of my life. I returned to work, took the letter, and ran it through the shredder. I started a blog and made myself accountable to the world, to train and ride in the 2012 Ride the Rockies: a 450+ mile bicycle tour through the mountains of Colorado. The world responded!!

A now dear friend from Texas committed to riding with me, and a few thousand readers visited my blog. After taking part in that ride, with a degree and background in marketing and communications, I set out to launch programs with the intent to lure people that don't normally ride a bicycle onto a bicycle. I was very ambitious and set lofty goals, all in a very public manner. Initially I gained a lot of traction, however the economic conditions at the time presented challenges that slowed progress, eventually, to a halt. I felt self-defeated, like a failure; however this time I sought help.

Confiding in friends led to one of them covering the costs for me to attend a three-day seminar designed to deliver a positive shift in the quality of your life. In this seminar, I came face-to-face with demons from my past and was finally able to take back the power I had given them. The lesson I learned through this seminar was the dynamic of a "vicious cycle." A dynamic where, internally, we give meaning to life events and then live our lives as if they were true. I was abused by my father as a child, and because of that I internalized that I was a burden and unlovable. Through the tears streaming down my face, I could see how these lies affected every relationship in my life. I didn't trust anyone, even myself, and it was the result of being stuck in a vicious cycle.

This was all perfect timing, because in September of 2016 an impossible prayer was answered when my wife gave birth to our first child, a beautiful perfect baby boy we named Sam. Beneath everything I knew I wasn't fit to be a dad, and for 49 years I hadn't been. Now at 50 I am a stay-at-home father.

During my wife's pregnancy I would start to freak myself out. What kind of father am I going to be? How am I ever going to discipline my son (the example I had really sucked)? In the past, these would have been paralyzing thoughts. I can't even imagine how I would have responded if this had would have happened in 2009. However, I now know I am prepared for whatever is going to happen, even if I don't yet realize it.

Every day I get to show my wife and son how much I love them. Every day I am glad I turned my bike around. What I learned was never be afraid or ashamed to ask for help, seek a mentor for guidance and accountability, take care of your body and always allow yourself time to be a kid, every day.

DeQuincy's Story: A Choice to Make Meaning

I remember the night I was "on top of the world" - I stood in the spotlight at my senior year of high school recognition assembly as the top-ranked male, having been offered a combined total of nearly half a million dollars in scholarship funding. I was heading off to an Ivy League school to study art and computer science. Having aced my advanced placement classes and scored in the upper percentiles on the SAT, I was in high demand. On my table at home were recruitment letters from universities including Brown, Harvard, Yale, Stanford, Amherst, and Berkeley. Admittedly, I smiled knowing that I was the envy of many of my peers as I prepared to step onto the stage. Did I have butterflies in my stomach? I'm sure I did, but they were glowing like neon signs. My family and friends were proud of me, and they cheered as I crossed the stage to receive my awards.

Fast forward just months later, and I was asking myself why I was even alive. I had left my family and community behind in Los Angeles to pursue my new life at college on the other side of the country. There were plenty of people around. They were incredibly smart and friendly. Indeed, the warmth of the students and faculty at Brown University was a major factor in my decision to enroll there. Nonetheless, I could not feel the love that was being offered. It was like it simply got sucked into an emotional black hole with no hope of return.

I thought that once I got to a new place, I would have the distance necessary to be able to turn my life around, and yet it was far more difficult than I could imagine. Is it possible to run far enough to escape the demons of personal history that haunt your memories and stalk your dreams? All the family issues I wanted to leave behind simply followed me to college. It was terribly frustrating to be unable to rapidly turn things around for myself. Then, on October 1st the value I placed on my life declined to the level that allowed for suicidal risk-taking. If my life didn't matter, then why continue pursuing an education or building new friendships? I took multiple risks that night, each with the chance of a fatal outcome. I'm sure that even then I wasn't completely sold on dying, but I hated life and would have been perfectly content with one of those gambles ending my life.

Once I was back in my dorm room, having survived my suicidal risks, I knew that I would later want to make sense of what was happening. Scribbling furiously, I tried to extract the pain in my head and nail it to my journal. Thankfully, my roommate stayed asleep. The heat from the small lamp on my desk was a welcome contrast to the chilly mist that had settled into Providence that night. I told myself that when I woke in the morning this surreal experience might feel like some bad dream, but I should remember that my desperate actions were now personal history, and not fictional drama.

After crossing that line at the start of October, my risk elevated, and I sank deeper and deeper into my depression. My best friend Mary Alice told me that she was so worried about me that she was seeing a therapist and encouraged me to go as well. Psychological Services was in Rhode Island Hall off the main quad and, following my friend's plea, I accepted that I needed help and went over to the antique white building. I wasn't sure what to expect as I climbed the stairs and pulled open the creaky wooden door. Avoiding eye-contact with students applying for Study Abroad programs on the first floor, I made my way over to the spiral staircase that led up to the second-floor counseling center. After suicidal thoughts were flagged on my intake forms, I was given an emergency appointment with Dr. Otoya. Though we only had a few sessions together, she turned out to be a good therapist, which was a critical experience in forming a positive view of mental health care.

Nonetheless, my friends eventually had to escalate the level of intervention by calling campus police to pick me up from the computer room where I was writing the goodbyes intended to precede a well-planned suicide. I was again seen by emergency crisis services that led up to time in a psychiatric hospital where a major turning point in my life occurred. However, the shift did not come by way of my individual or group therapy, medications, or scheduled activities. I left the hospital with a determination to be a mental health advocate because I wanted the other patients I met to have a chance to get better and get out of the hospital. At the end of my three day stay at the hospital the glass double-doors opened, and I stepped out into the frozen wonderland that is December in New England. As I trudged through the thick snow to catch a bus back to campus, the wind assailing my nose and only the pads on my headphones supplying shelter for my ears, I swore to do all I could for my peers. Destiny had pointed me toward a life in mental health advocacy.

Yet, while destiny may have helped guide my career direction, fate also had cruel twists in store. Tragically, as I crossed the country back to California for winter break in my first year of college, my therapist was flying to Columbia when the plane went down in the mountains killing almost everyone on board, including Dr. Otoya and her family. I only learned about her death when I returned to campus in January. How does someone make sense of that type of loss? I was incredibly tempted to conclude that I somehow invited calamity into my life and bad things were bound to keep happening. However, I settled on the belief that my therapist's unwavering belief that I still had a lot to contribute to the world held even more value for me as a precious memory.

Fate was not yet finished with me, though. I also lost my best friend Mary Alice a few years later. I very clearly remember coming back home after a trip to Catalina Island and hearing the voicemail from her sister, saying that nobody had heard from her in a while and they were worried. My heart sank. I knew that something had gone terribly wrong. I feared the worst and yet held on to the hope that she may have just been on the run and would call to say that she was safe. That hope evaporated as time passed without any contact from my friend. Her ex-boyfriend was arrested and in court he revealed how he lured her in, then murdered her and disposed of her body in a local landfill never to be seen again. How does someone recover from that kind of traumatic loss? The pain has dulled over the years, but I'm not sure I can ever completely get back to where I was before. Nonetheless, I had to somehow find meaning amid the suffering to regain control of my narrative.

Losing Mary Alice carried multiple messages for me as I tried to move forward. Admittedly, some were not initially positive. I wondered if I was doomed to lose friends, or if I was somehow a harbinger of death for those who might become connected to me. I mostly avoided forming close friendships with others for years. On the other hand, I also felt that if I died by suicide, then it would negate her efforts to save me and thus tarnish her legacy. Alternatively, each positive contribution I could make would in some way add to her story. That choice – to either add to the tragedy of her death or become a conduit for the continuation of her benevolence – was instrumental to my survival. Like my college therapist, Mary Alice died believing in me, and only I had the power to honor that belief and prove them right.

I have endured other traumatic losses in my life, sudden deaths of people close to me. At one time I told my most recent therapist that the lesson was that anything good in my life could be taken away at any moment without warning. There is truth to that. All we really have for certain is the present moment. Yet, I eventually came to a broader conclusion: radical events that significantly alter your life can happen at any moment without prior notice. Sometimes those events are painful, but not always. Good things can happen that way too. I have been fortunate enough to cross paths with some extraordinary people who chose to have incredible life adventures, and sometimes those choices come with dramatic endings.

Not all the major shifts in my life have been tied to loss. There was a pivotal point in high school when a relatively new program arrived on campus, recruited me, and changed my post-secondary trajectory in the direction of the Ivy League college I eventually graduated from. There was also a key moment when a kind couple from Georgia answered my inquisitive email in a way that catalyzed my advocate spirit, sparked my career in suicide prevention, and set the foundation for lifelong friendships. Later, there was a critical intervention when I was again seriously considering ending my life and, in rapid succession, I got an invitation to speak in Australia (a place I had wanted to visit since childhood), and I was informed that I was to be honored with an award for my advocacy work.

I was proud of what I had accomplished thus far in suicide prevention as I walked onto stage to get that Lifeline Achievement Voice Award from SAMHSA (Substance Abuse and

Mental Health Services Administration). This time the recognition carried more weight because in my mind it was shared with people in my life who could only attend the ceremony in spirit. While that award was based on nearly two decades of work in suicide prevention, my work wouldn't have been possible without my friend's unwavering support, my therapist believing in me, and all the decisions that helped transform painful experiences in a meaningful direction.

I do believe that our experiences, painful or positive, happen for a reason. I think we get to choose what the reason is. Life presents us with all manner of events, but at the end of the day it's still our story to write. The next phase of my life journey is helping others who have personal experience with suicidal crisis to understand it, make meaning of it, and use it as a source for growing stronger.

BUILDING YOUR MENTAL MECHANIC'S TOOLBOX

PART I

TOOL #1: Assemble Your A-Team Pit Crew

Your pit crew are people who have your back and you have theirs. When working well, your pit crew is standing by ready to roll up their sleeves and lend a hand to get you back on track. Everyone should have at least three people (better to have 10+) they can call at 3 O'clock in the morning when things can seem most bleak. It's best to figure out who is in your pit crew before the tires come flying off, so let's think about who the best candidates are now. These could be friends from childhood, battle buddies, or cherished family members. Whomever they are, it's probably a good idea to let them know that they are on your A-Team (and maybe develop a code word to let them know when you need to connect urgently). Answer these questions to help you think about who your crew members might be.

See if you can name at least ten people:

- Who makes you feel good about yourself?

    _____

- Who brings out the best in you?

    _____

- Who knows the "real" you?

    _____

- Who would support you even if it meant they were inconvenienced?

    _____

- Who is a good listener?

- Who do you trust?

- Who has "walked a mile in your shoes"?

- Who put the bomp in the bomp bah bomp bah bomp, who put the ram in the rama lama ding dong?

Now that you have a list of people, text or call each one and let them know how much they mean to you. Let them know you were thinking about them. Maybe set up a time to get together - just one-on-one - in the next few weeks.

Daily practices in preventive maintenance are necessary to build our mental machine. We also need to do tune ups and scheduled maintenance: reassess, regroup, recycle, and renew frequently and consistently. You're either getting better or getting worse, there's no idling, and no standing still.

TOOL #2: Inflating Your Wellness Wheel

When most of us think about the term "wellness," we think about nutrition and fitness, but total wellness is much more than that. Look at your calendar and your bank balance - these are indicators of how you're valuing different aspects of your well-being.

Self-assess where you are on each area of the wheel with 0 being at the center of the wheel (no air in that part) and 10 being as good as it gets (fully inflated). Chances are that your wheel is a bit unevenly filled, or it's wearing unevenly - that can make for a bumpy ride!

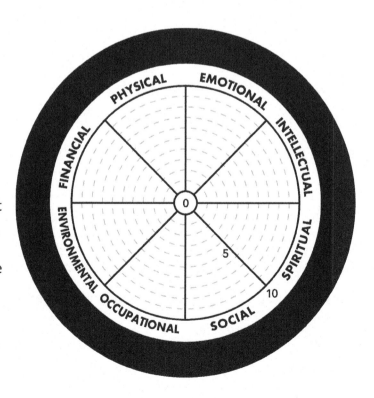

- Social: How we get along with others.

- Spiritual: How we make meaning in our lives and live in our values.

- Emotional: How we experience our emotions and cope.

- Occupational: How we find fulfillment and balance in our work lives.

- Intellectual: How we continue to learn new things.

- Physical: How we take care of our bodies.

- Financial: How we manage our money now and for the future.

- Environmental: How we are connected to the earth and communities around us.

Now see if you can make at least one new commitment in each category over the next 30-days:

- Social:

- Spiritual:

- Emotional:

- Occupational:

- Intellectual:

- Physical:

- Financial:

- Environmental:

TROUBLESHOOTING

CHAPTER 3: TROUBLESHOOTING

Troubleshooting is about catching emerging problems early and getting yourself back on track before they progress into something more serious. All of us experience life challenges - sometimes we can fix things ourselves, and sometimes we need a little help along the way. That's why God created AAA.

"Show me how to fix myself. How to stitch up my own wound like Rambo."

This quote came from one of our focus group participants when asked what men needed to address their mental health challenges. Many of our guys said something to the effect of, "Before you send us to go see a mental health professional, give us the tools to understand 'how bad is it?" and then a self-help kit to try some new things to see if we can solve our own problems."

This reasoning is probably why some guys take auto shop class in high school. They want to learn what can go wrong with a car, what tools are needed to maintain and fix a vehicle, and how to do routine maintenance and make repairs - on their own.

We get it. There are many reasons why reaching out for treatment from a psychiatrist, psychologist, or other professional counselor might be daunting. In this section we offer things you can do to help yourself plus so-called "alternative therapies" that can help you cope when self-help isn't quite enough.

Instead of troubleshooting when that unusual rattle starts emerging from somewhere under the car, we ignore the problem and start to notice all the other jalopies around us. This human tendency of social comparison can often get us in trouble. We start to surround ourselves with people who are in worse shape than we are, so we seem normal or even healthy by comparison. It's a common refrain among any number of folks who attend 12-Step Meetings, "I go to feel good about myself, because most everyone else there is far worse off than I am. I'm screwed up, but not THAT screwed up."

Sometimes our cars have problems we know should be fixed but we put off doing anything about it for a variety of reasons. We minimize the problem. Sure, the check engine light is on, but that could mean anything from a loose gas cap, to a bad oxygen sensor, to a catalytic converter that needs to be replaced. We don't have the time or the money to fix whatever it is. We temporarily "solve" the problem with a piece of electrical tape placed over the warning light. Out of sight, out of mind.

Back in the day, they used to be called "Idiot Lights," because before there were computers in cars, they wouldn't come on unless some problem with your car had reached critical mass. The problem had reached critical mass because the idiot driver wasn't performing the proper routine maintenance. Nowadays, with the advent of computers in cars, these lights warn of trouble, in most cases long before any real damage is done.

Wouldn't it be great if humans had warning lights? If we all had a little built in mini dashboard? Like a Low Fuel light that came on to let you know it was time to eat because your blood sugar was low, or a Battery Warning light that sprang to life when you were running out of energy and needed to take a break to recharge, or how about an Engine Temperature light that glowed when you were on the verge of losing your temper and should add some "coolant" to the situation, or do something else to blow off a little steam.

And finally, what if when you were about to fall off the wagon, or relapse on drugs, or start smoking again because you felt like you just couldn't help yourself, your mental brakes began to squeak, with the sound of metal on metal, like worn out brakes on a car do? It would be the signal that your willpower is wearing thin, and that you need help replacing your mental brake pads and rotors, otherwise the day may come when you CANNOT stop yourself.

What if we could just drop into our local grease monkey's shop, crawl up onto the lift, and let them look under our mental hood. Sometimes with a car it's as simple as a loose bolt, and other times it as serious as the engine that is three quarts low on oil, about to freeze up and needing to be replaced. Sometimes with us, it's simply that we need a good night's sleep, and other times it's as serious as us being on the verge of a mental crisis needing hospitalization.

Either way, paying attention to the warning signs and doing what you can to fix it right away, to mitigate any damage, will give both you and your car a longer, more worry-free life. As the gas station attendant in the old Esso commercials used to say, "Happy motoring!"

After-Market Safety Equipment

The troubleshooting stage of mental health maintenance is both about catching the problems when they are emerging AND addressing them with low level interventions to get yourself back in action. Sometimes you need a few tools in your trunk to get the job done. Here are a few DIY resources we recommend:

First Aid Kit:

Everyone should have a first aid kit in their car. You won't be able to do open-heart surgery or perform an emergency appendectomy on the side of the road, but you will be able to stop the bleeding and dress the cut you got trying to loosen the lug nuts. There's a reason it's called FIRST Aid. It's just the first step. Dress the wound and then get professional help. A safe care plan if there's a crisis works exactly the same way; it won't fix the underlying problem but will allow you to maintain until professional help is available. Think of it as a highly effective mental Band-Aid. Some of the items in your "psychological first aid kit" or "roadside repair" toolbox are various emotional regulation and cognitive reframing tactics you will learn later in this chapter. Sometimes, a little first aid is all you need to prevent infection and allow for natural healing.

Flares:

A lot of car safety kits come with flares, or reflective stand up triangles to warn approaching drivers of dangers ahead. That way other drivers can be more aware, lower their speed, and offer help if needed. It would be a good idea to have mental emergency flares or reflective triangles to warn others as they approach that all is not well with you. For some, flares can be code words you communicate to others when you need more support. Something you can text to your pit crew that means, "Come on over and hang out" or, "Call me later tonight, I could use company."

Jumper Cables:

Sometimes, the car is well maintained and finely tuned and the tank is full of the proper fuel, but when you turn the key nothing happens. Uh-oh, you've got a dead battery. Which is a bit of a misnomer. Usually it's not dead, it's just drained. You did something, like leave the lights on, that used up all the juice with no way to replenish it. So what do you do? You break out the jumper cables and charge your battery up enough to get it started again. Our mental batteries get drained as well. Too much to do, in too little time, with too little help, and no way to replenish can run down the best of us. Activities, like therapy, peer support, taking a mental health day, and the proper meds can get you jump-started when your mental batteries are drained. Or, if you're old enough to remember cars with a manual transmission, roll started - no jumper cables needed.

We offer two strategies for how best to flag men with emerging issues; one for you, and one for the people around you.

Screening:

We screen for emissions problems. We check for compression in the engine. We screen for cholesterol. We screen for blood pressure. We need to be screened for depression, substance use and suicidal thoughts. Usually these screening tools are anonymous and confidential, and many can now be found online. They take just a couple of minutes to complete, and they roughly sort people into two categories: "It's likely that you're okay for now," and, "We probably should have another conversation with a professional to see if there is an issue here." The best online screening tools will then refer you to some resources that apply to your needs.

Many excellent screening tools exists, including the 20-point head inspection at Man Therapy - www.ManTherapy.org. Go ahead - give it a whirl and see, "How bad is it?" regarding your mental health. Because we know that people living with suicidal thoughts are more likely to go to their medical doctor than a mental health professional, more primary care doctors are asking questions about depression, anxiety, and even suicide at routine medical appointments.

When a warning light on your car dashboard begins to glow, run that puppy in for screening. It's a simple process nowadays, and not a lot of guesswork. They plug your car's computer into the diagnostic computer, and it spits out a code or two that tells the mechanic exactly what the problem is. Wouldn't it be great if diagnosing what was bothering you was that simple? A light comes on, you make an appointment, plop down on the examining table, a tech comes by and connects your brain to their diagnostic computer, and out pop a couple of codes.

If you have an issue that stays undiagnosed and unaddressed, it's only going to get worse. Why not prepare in advance for mental emergencies by assembling a mental health first aid kit? Gather mental health first aid tools, put together a mental health first aid kit, so if you start to have the warning signs of a mental breakdown coming on, you have a mental health first aid action plan.

Gatekeeper Training:

Imagine, if you will, that there's a gate around your mechanic's lot and you need to get your car inside to have it checked out. The gatekeeper would be the one to open the gate and let you in.

It's sort of an unfortunate name, because in some places a "gatekeeper" keeps people out of a system or opportunity (like insurance gatekeepers). In the case of mental health, the term "gatekeeper" often refers to someone who can open the gate to important conversations about despair and suicide.

Gatekeeper trainings teach people how to have conversations that offer compassion and that connect people to mental health resources. Any adult (and sometimes teens) can take the training. There are a few models of the training like QPR (Question, Persuade, Refer) and safeTALK that take between an hour to 3 ⅓ hours to complete. These trainings cover warning signs and risk factors and how to engage in effective dialogue that links people to help. One of the most important aspects of the trainings is that there are opportunities to practice, because it turns out having these conversations is more difficult than you would imagine.

In many ways gatekeeper training is like CPR. We train as many people as possible to have their eyes on the field, ready to notice any concerning behavior that might signal the need for a response. The people who have had the training feel a sense of competence and confidence that they know what to do. When they see someone in distress, they step in and compassionately sustain the life of the person in crisis until supports are reached.

These trainings can be offered to workplaces, faith communities, social associations like rotaries, and local affiliations like chambers of commerce.

Your Psychological Roadside Repair Kit: Emotional Regulation and Thinking Skills

Once a problem has been found, now we need to go into our first aid kit and find the resources to get us back on the road. Self-help tools are everywhere, but not all of them are evidence-based. Here are some to get you started. Many of these are based in a therapy called Dialectical Behavior Therapy (DBT), a skills-based form of treatment that has been shown to successfully help people manage their emotions and relationships with other people.

When you hear that rattle under the hood or see your personal check engine light glow, pull over and try these DIY strategies out:

Opposite action:

Intense emotions like shame, rage, and despair can create an urge for us to act. Sometimes these actions cause additional problems. Opposite action is a skill to apply during these times. The steps are: notice the emotion, then ask yourself if the emotion is justified and if the intensity is helpful. If the answer to either of those criteria is "no," then do something that gives you the opposite emotion.

This is a little bit like the old story about the guy who was pulled over by the cops for speeding. When asked why he was going so fast he said, "I'm almost out of gas and I was rushing to get to the gas station." Of course, if he'd asked himself if this action was helpful, he might have realized that the answer is no, because the faster he goes, the more gas he burns more quickly. Perhaps if he had done something just the opposite, like slow down and coast when he could, he would have made the gas go farther and not gotten stopped by the cops.

Improving the moment:

While we usually can't fix our biggest problems easily, there are several things we can do to improve the moment that will help us shift from distress to calm. Getting focused on one thing that can shift the moment - breathing, fresh air, petting the dog, imagining a tranquil scene - helps the brain slow down and improves mood.

How many times have you found yourself in gridlock and felt your blood pressure surge? You could choose to sit there enraged about something you can do nothing about, or you could improve the moment. Put on your favorite song and sing to it at the top of your lungs. Enjoy a piece of gum. Daydream about your next vacation. Create funny stories in your head about the people stuck in traffic in the car next to you. Smile ironically at them and shrug; you're both in this situation together.

Challenging thoughts:

Many of us have negative thoughts about ourselves and the world that are connected to feelings and behaviors that keep us stuck. When we challenge our negative thoughts, we ask ourselves, "Is there substantial evidence for my thought?" "Is there evidence contrary to my thought?" "Am I attempting to interpret this situation without all the evidence?" "Would my mechanic think that what sounds like a monkey under my hood banging on the engine is a bad thing?" When we slow down and challenge our thinking, we often can discover new conclusions.

Behavioral activation:

When we are depressed, we can feel our energy is too sapped to get out and enjoy life. This leads us to feel even more isolated and worthless in a vicious cycle. Committing to your friends, family, and to yourself to get up and do something you like is a first step in getting out of the rut. Write down some activities that you used to or still enjoy and schedule them in your day or week (e.g., taking a walk, going to a sporting event, or going fishing). Getting active and having a change of scenery can do wonders to alleviate the doldrums. Usually, only the first steps of motivation are the hardest, and once you are engaged in the activity, mood improves.

When you're putting off getting your poorly-running car looked at, for whatever reason, sometimes the longest mile is the one from your driveway to the dealership. Just because you have the car evaluated, doesn't mean you have to make all the repairs the mechanic recommends. Generally, there's a list of those that can wait and a list of those that need immediate attention. Knowing is better than not knowing, and the way to know is to evaluate.

Distraction:

Sometimes we are not able to get out to do an enjoyable activity, but we can do something that interrupts the stream of negative thoughts. We can crank up loud music, play solitaire on our phone, call an old friend, or make prank phone calls (okay, kidding about the prank calls... but I'll bet Prince Albert is still in the can). These distractions are short-lived and not meant to solve anything; they just help us pull away from the rut we are in to let the negative thoughts die down for a bit.

Self-soothing:

When we feel agitated or anxious, sometimes it's helpful to get our bodies and mind more relaxed by engaging in behaviors that comfort us: a hot shower, a cup of soup, a warm blanket, listening to a relaxation visualization on the phone (there are many great apps). These behaviors are likely to help you take the edge off so you can think more clearly.

Taking a break:

One of the challenges to our mental health is the fact that we are bombarded every moment of the day with a long list of demands and information coming at us from all angles. Taking a break might be stepping away from your phone or computer for a couple of hours (or a weekend). It could be carving out one day a week to focus on self-care and rest. It could be taking a vacation and going "off the grid" completely for a week. Or it could be taking an extended sabbatical, where for a couple of months you clear your head and regroup.

Paced Breathing:

Breathing is essential to so many of our self-care practices like yoga and meditation. It can also be used to help us get through difficult moments in our day. One breathing technique that many people find helpful to improve concentration and performance and release stress is called "box breathing." Breathe deeply and slowly through your nose to the count of four and notice how your lungs fill and your belly inflates. Hold for four seconds and slowly exhale for the count of four. Leave your lungs empty to the count of four and repeat by slowly filling your lungs. Imagine tracing a line around a box with each step. 4 x 4 x 4 x 4

Breathe in for the count of 4

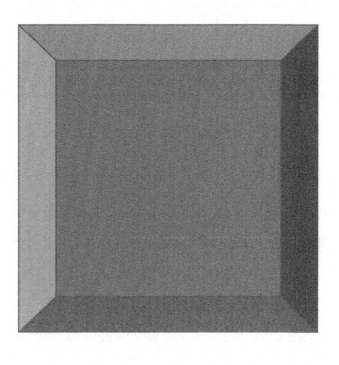

Hold for the count of 4

Hold for the count of 4

Breathe out for the count of 4

85

Dive Reflex:

When you were a kid, did you ever jump fully into a pool or a lake that was very cold? Do you remember what happened next? You probably found yourself in some sort of shock when you came up for air. This reaction is called the "Mammalian Dive Reflex." From an evolutionary perspective this reflex preferentially distributes oxygen to the heart and brain, allowing us to stay underwater for longer periods of time. It also kicks in our parasympathetic nervous system that slows our heart rate down very quickly. Submerging your face in a bowl of icy water or taking a cold shower and letting the water hit your face just below the eyes produces the same response. There was even a version of this when some of us were kids. It involved a toilet bowl full of cold water, and it was called "a swirlie." Bullies found it very therapeutic - the rest of us not so much.

Sometimes we can practice all these self-help skills and more and still feel immobilized and overwhelmed. It's like having your rear-wheel drive car stuck in the mud; the more gas you give it, the more stuck your car becomes. Maybe you are at this stage, but just not quite ready to make a call for professional mental health treatment. Here are some other sources of support you can reach out to as you consider what might work best for you.

Troubleshooters in Your Midst

If you're not prepared, say you don't have the jumper cables, you can find someone with a strong back who can give you a push down a hill to roll-start your engine. Once you're rolling, you can turn the key, pop the clutch, and the car will roar to life. Sometimes almost anyone can help you with a problem, and other times it takes someone with the proper qualifications.

Peer Support

We talked about the resilience-boosting effects of the pit crew earlier in the book, but many men also find formal peer support is a very effective troubleshooting strategy when problems are emerging. Peer specialists or peer supporters are doing the work they do because they have the expertise of having lived through overwhelming experiences and have a perspective of what it takes to get to the other side. They can offer you some new perspectives on your own stressful situation and will let you know that you are not alone.

Twelve-step groups are an obvious example for people experiencing consequences from their substance use, gambling, or sexual behavior. Other peer support resources might be accessed through your local chapter of the "Depression-Bipolar Support Alliance" or "National Alliance on Mental Illness." In rare cases, peer support programs might be available through your workplace or professional associations (sometimes also known as "member assistance programs").

The Defense Centers of Excellence[26] generated a report on best practices in peer support that may help you find a peer support resource that is effective and trustworthy. In their research on peer support programs in military and Veterans communities, they found that the best peer supporters were selected because of their communication skills, like empathy and active listening, their trustworthy character, and their positive role modeling. With role clarity, training, and supervision these formal peer supporters could effectively deliver the "key ingredients" of social support, experiential life lessons, a trustworthy and confidential bond, and easy access when support was needed.

Intentional Peer Support[27] is another model of thinking about formal peer support that focuses on cultivating transforming relationships that move all peers towards lives worth living by deeply understanding how trauma and toxic environments play a role. Here peers develop a greater awareness of their interpersonal patterns, and then they challenge one another to try new things to grow.

Leadership Coaching

Leadership coaching is a one-to-one personalized consultation service that helps people develop plans for short- and long-term personal and professional goals. Often the leaders being coached explore things like personal branding, motivation, and interpersonal strategies that help them become more effective. While under the guise of building ability in business, leadership coaches often understand how the professional and personal lives are intertwined. So, while not therapy per se, sometimes leadership coaching focuses on personal growth. It's like "therapy light" and usually far less threatening for many men. According to "Next Level Leadership Coaching[28]" it's estimated that over 60% of Fortune 500 CEO's benefit from leadership coaches.

Many CEOs take part in something called Vistage. It's a networking organization where C-Level executives, of similarly sized companies, meet once a week to share problems and perspectives on solving those problems, like a business peer counseling group. Just because you're the boss, doesn't mean you don't need a helping hand now and then. They generally have a speaker presenting every month on topics of interest, including mental health, to C-Level executives.

Pastoral Care

Men who may not consider seeking professional mental health services initially may find it acceptable to speak with a trusted confidant within their faith community. "Pastoral" comes from the idea of being shepherded - cared for and protected. Many faith traditions have a person or group of people standing by to provide counsel and emotional and spiritual guidance for members going through difficult life challenges. Sometimes faith communities also offer spiritual support groups organized by age, gender, or life experience that can help people find support. Many people in the role of pastoral caregiving have received training on mental health literacy and how to be effective counselors. Many are bound by similar levels of confidentiality as other mental health providers. Ask if your faith community provides these services and, if so, ask the pastoral support to see if it would be a good fit:

- Do they see emotional problems as a moral failing?

- Do they think emotional crises are related to demons or lack of faith?

- How would they work collaboratively with mental health services?

- What is their training around mental health literacy and helping people through depression, anxiety, addiction, and so on?

- What would they do if someone told them they were thinking about suicide?

- What do they believe about suicide?

Animal-Assisted Therapy

If you've ever owned a pet you loved, you have felt the power of animals to give comfort. Over the past decade, this form of support has evolved into a much sought-after addition to, or in some cases alternative to, mental health treatment. The animals - dogs, horses, even cats, pigs, birds, and llamas - are used to help people with various mental health challenges. Levels of training and intervention skills for these animals fluctuate greatly. Some "therapy animals" provide the comfort of companionship, while others are highly-trained service animals that can do things like gently wake and comfort a Veteran who is experiencing a traumatic nightmare. At these higher levels of intervention, the animals (usually dogs) are carefully selected, trained for months, and then thoughtfully paired with their care recipient.

Each of these tools and resources can be beneficial in helping men "over the bumps in life." Like many things, not all will work for everyone. Sometimes trial-and-error experimentation can help you figure out which is best for you. More than one guy has decided that he could save money by doing his own car repair and maintenance and has done so successfully. On the other hand, plenty of guys have tried that only to realize that the better course would be to earn the money to pay the mechanic, who knows how to do it right the first time. Here are some stories of men who have found their ways through unimaginable grief and trauma by using some of the coping strategies mentioned here.

Meet the Mental Mechanics of Troubleshooting

John L's Story - Losing a Child to Addiction

I always had an idea that I would be in a profession of helping others. I really liked medicine and psychology from as far back as I can remember. I was interested in how biology and interpersonal interactions shaped our thoughts and behavior. I originally had planned to go into medicine and become a physician, but I did not apply myself as an undergraduate to the extent that I should have to get accepted into medical school. I took some time off and then decided that the profession of nursing would be right for me. It allowed me to use my interest in science along with my understanding of the importance of interpersonal relationships in gaining trust and acceptance.

It wasn't long after I was licensed as a registered nurse that my wife and I decided that we would start a family. This was going to be great! My wife is also a registered nurse, and with our combined talent and interpersonal skills we were ready to become great parents. We read all the expert books and learned how to raise successful children. During her pregnancy we made sure that we played classical music and read books to my first child while he was still in utero. We were ready to raise the perfect child.

When Timothy was born, I remember the feeling of being overwhelmed by the responsibility and the promise of raising a family. As any new parent, I'm sure I had my doubts about what the next step was. I came to the quick realization that despite all I had read I was not fully prepared for what I was about to embark on.

As Tim grew, I came to understand that most of parenting is learned through on-the-job training. When he was young it was easy to decide what was right or wrong as far as teaching my son and keeping him safe. As he grew older, parenting became much more complicated. Decisions were no longer clearly right or wrong but fell within the spectrum of shades of gray. As he reached his teenage years, I soon realized that there were larger forces at work, many of which had influences on my son which I could not control.

In his junior year of high school he developed, rather quickly, severe depression and a panic disorder. He withdrew, isolated, and struggled with his emotions. The psychiatric professional in me jumped into high gear and made sure Tim got a proper evaluation and plan for treatment. I felt that if we got him professional help right away, we were going to handle this problem and get him through it. Tim did not respond very well to the proposed treatment of antidepressants and psychotherapy. He still struggled to get through most days. As a parent I was completely bewildered. I was used to stepping in and fixing these problems so that my son would not have to suffer. That was what a father does for his family. It was very difficult for me to accept that I could not help my son nor protect him from the emotional pain he struggled with.

The feeling of powerlessness was demoralizing.

My feelings of helplessness and impotence were then magnified when Tim began using opiates to ease his emotional pain. I could not believe that this was happening in my family. What kind of father was I? My oldest son become addicted to heroin? I often vented my frustration at him. My anger climbed as I felt less effective as a father. My anger blinded me to the pain that he was in and instead made me blame him for not trying hard enough to beat this problem.

On morning in January 2016, I was awakened by a phone call at 5:00 AM. It was a doctor from the local hospital emergency room. He told me that Tim was brought in after cardiac arrest due to an overdose of heroin. Of course, I was in shock but immediately sprang into action. My wife and I met my other son at the hospital to find that Tim was unresponsive and on a ventilator.

Within 36 hours we were forced to make the decision to turn off Tim's life-support.

He had been showing signs of worsening brain damage and there was no hope of any positive resolution. At this time, we - my wife, my younger son, and I - were forced to make the most agonizing decision of our lives. We had to decide whether to let Tim go on indefinitely without any hope of returning brain function or ability for him to breathe on his own. We knew Tim would not have chosen that kind of life (if you can call that life). We decided to ask the medical staff to turn off the ventilator and let Tim pass. We held Tim's hands and kissed him softly until his heart stopped about five minutes later.

At that moment, my life was changed forever.

I had heard another parent speak who also lost a child. He described his life as being experienced in two separate chapters. He had a life before he lost a child and then another life after the loss of his child. I now know exactly what he meant. It is impossible for me to describe the pain, the doubt, and the guilt that I experience on a continual basis. It is now almost two years since Tim died, and at this time I struggle to find any belief that life is going to get better. I also feel guilt that I despair over what I have lost, separate from my loss of my son.

Before Tim died, my wife and I had reached that point in our life where our two sons were grown adults and not so dependent on us. We were able to experience the opportunity to spend time together, travel, and come and go as we pleased. We were happy for the availability of more time to devote to our relationship. Now the joy and promise that we had found for us is gone. I feel there is little hope of that returning.

That is a loss that I think of daily. At this point, it is a struggle to get up every day and get through the day. I feel guilty that I am thinking of how my life has changed for the worse, when my oldest son has lost his life, and my wife and younger son suffer horribly every day themselves. Is it selfish that I feel pain for the loss of what life had recently promised?

I also struggle with the guilt of how I treated Tim during his struggles with depression and drug addiction. My frustration with not knowing how to help him was acted out in my relationship with him. There were moments that I felt nurturing and sensitive for his struggles. They were also moments where I felt he was not trying hard enough and was disappointing me.

I struggle every day with the realization that I may have reinforced Tim's belief that he was a loser and a disappointment to his parents. I know there were times when I gave him the message that he was a disappointment to me. I struggle now with the knowledge that addiction is a disease and not a choice. I now realize that Tim was doing the best that he could but could not figure out another way for himself. I wish I had known that then. I wish I could've been more supportive and loving to him and made him feel worthwhile. I can never get that chance back. I despair in the belief that Tim died feeling he was a disappointment to his father. I don't know how to overcome this.

The other message I have clearly learned is that it turns out a parent has much less control over their child's life than I ever imagined before I had children. As I stated earlier, I had planned to be a good parent and raise a successful child. It's hard to feel confident as a parent when your oldest child struggled so much emotionally that he needed to turn to heroin for some relief and died from his need to escape his pain.

Since Tim died, I have devoted all my time outside of work to helping those suffering from mental illness and addiction. I have started a nonprofit organization with the mission of reducing the shame and stigma of mental illness and addiction and promoting the mental, physical, and psychological health of our community. I often speak out at community forums about the reality of the heroin problem and how it affects good people from good families. I tell the story of my son's struggle and untimely death as an example of how this epidemic is experienced throughout every community. I am extremely fortunate in that my extended family and in-laws have been incredibly supportive of this initiative. Many of them give long hours of their time to help our cause. My efforts in this cause have resulted in my meeting many other parents who have lost a child to addiction. This is a group I wished I never had a reason to belong to. I can see others experiencing their grief in a multitude of ways. Some, at least on the outside, appeared to be very well-adjusted and focused. Others carry their pain in more obvious ways. I wonder how I appear to them.

It is also important to note how this grief has affected my marriage. My wife and I, like many other men and women, experience our grief and emotions in very different ways. She is more overtly demonstrative of her pain, and I tend to hold it in with only occasional bursts of crying.

I know she wishes I would talk to her more about what I am experiencing emotionally, but at times I experience the emotions without words. It is just a feeling of sadness that envelops me when I least expect it. It's not always possible to articulate clearly what is going on in my head or my heart. I know this increases her feeling of distance from me. Other times, as I did in relationship to Timothy, my frustration comes out in anger and irritability. Unfortunately, my wife is usually the recipient of these unpleasant emotions. I act like this even though I deeply need to feel my connection with her. The strength of our relationship has gotten us through much struggle over our lives and I'm not sure I can continue without her support. I still need to figure out a way to not let my feelings create a barrier between us.

For the past 17 months I have been focusing on working to reduce the shame and stigma of addiction and mental illness. I have been traveling the state of Connecticut speaking out about the realities of addiction and how it happens to good people from good families. I have trained groups about the medical explanation of addiction and its treatment. I am trying hard to make something positive come from Tim's struggle and death. This is part of how I cope with my grief. I think that at times this endeavor is a distraction, and I need to try hard to not allow this distraction to be my only coping mechanism.

At the time I am writing this, I am still in the depths of grief. I am overcome at times by the dread that my life will not get better; that I will never again experience a sense of hope when looking toward the future. I have just made the decision to enter psychotherapy. As this is what I do for a living, it has become obvious to me that I am not getting better on my own. I will not lie and say that I feel confident that this is going to be the answer to my struggles, but I know I need to try. I need to try not just for myself but for my wife and my younger son. I do not know if I will feel any true happiness about my life again, but I know I need to try to be there to support my wife and son.

Jeremy's Story: Wounded by Grief

Plato has been quoted as saying, "The unexamined life is not worth living." I completely agree with this sentiment. Vital to our being is the need to search for purpose, while making sense of the obstacles in our path toward wisdom. Barriers come in many forms. A childhood of neglect, emotional trauma, and loss trained me to question everything and everyone. Growing up as the oldest of three children, with a single mother struggling to overcome her demons of abuse and abandonment, trained me to also survive and provide for the needs of others. The blessings of my grandparents provided me with a faith capable of carrying me through it all. As I continue to examine my life and the purpose of suffering, I find myself thankful for my journey.

My grandfather had his own experience with trauma. He experienced the loss of both his parents before the age of 18, the loss of two children before he was 65, and yet he was still able to raise three grandchildren out of the grace of his own heart. He decided to sacrifice his life, so we might have one. My grandfather remained my exemplar, as I became a collegiate athlete, Soldier, Doctor of Physical Therapy, and now an Assistant Professor. He was the epitome of a selfless servant and my best friend. I was determined to give my life to continuing his legacy of selfless service to both my country and my fellow man.

As I sat on a plane leaving Afghanistan on emergency leave to be at the bedside of my grandfather, or what the Army called my "in loco parentis," my mind began to race with questions that riddled my soul. Since childhood, my grandfather was my guide, friend, counselor, and only source of stability. Although I am married with three children, it was a final bedside hug that my grandfather and I shared as his favorite song played that will forever be ingrained in my memory.

After being awake for 36 hours straight, transitioning flights between Afghanistan, Kuwait, Ireland, and the United States to finally land in my hometown of Baton Rouge, LA, I began to feel emotionally numb. I had only felt this way once before: after receiving a call from my grandfather 15 years earlier that my mother had died of suicide. I was able to rationalize that her soul was finally at peace, as life for her on earth was a constant struggle. Using my strength of intellect and logic, I was able to comfort myself and overcome this numb feeling. It's a pattern I've used to cope my entire life.

This instance was different. There was no rational explanation for why my grandfather would be perfectly fine in January but be in hospice in June. I arrived at the hospice facility exhausted, yet grateful that I could be with my grandfather. Carrying in my right arm an encased American flag that had been flown in his honor over our forward operating base, I looked my grandfather in the face, smiled, and saw the gravity of the situation. It was obvious that he was waiting for me to arrive, so I might give him one last hug. He mustered up enough energy to stand from his bed and smiled as if his life was now complete, while The

Old Rugged Cross played on his CD player. A day later, I lay my head on his chest, fell asleep for the first time in 48 hours, and was awakened by the nurse telling me, "I think he has passed away."

I would return to war a different man than I left. I was no longer a servant willing to serve at my own expense. I was now broken. Wounded by grief causing me to reassess my core values and beliefs. Why would a good and loving God take away my best friend, all while I was serving our country as part of my calling? What was the meaning of this grief? How might I walk away from this a better person? These were the questions that riddled my soul. A couple of weeks after I returned, our brigade suffered the loss of four Soldiers, all of which I knew and treated as patients, to a donkey-borne IED (Improvised Explosive Device). As I stared at the night sky during one of their hero ceremonies, I began to feel myself slip into an even darker place. Everyone around me seemed to be affected as well, but no one showed signs of emotional processing. For the most part, everyone dropped their heads, turned around and went on about their work. I did the same.

For the next 18 months, I poured myself into my work. Perhaps it was an attempt, although not a conscious one, to avoid dealing with the emotional pain of my experience. While work seemed to be keeping my emotions at bay, my physical body began to feel the toil. I became ill, wasn't sleeping more than four hours at night, and experienced anger and rage like I'd never experienced before. The lowest point occurred when I was diagnosed with a severe sinus infection and given a medication that set my brain on fire. I couldn't run away from my thoughts, grief, and general feeling of anxiety any longer. I called my boss and told him my mind was too cluttered to even drive to work. It was as if every emotion I should have processed over the past 18 months exploded at once. He arranged for me to see some-one in our behavioral health clinic, and my recovery process began.

The last three years have been filled with highs and lows, but the trend line has been in a positive direction. Prayer, meditation, journaling, counseling, and my loving spouse have carried me through my struggle. I've spent a great deal of time asking the question, "Why?" I've found that a better question is to ask, "What?"

What is it that life is teaching me? What is it that I have been predestined to do? Because of my experience, I can now empathize with others and embrace them during their times of struggle. Instead of searching for meaning by looking at the lives of others, I can now offer hope to others – because of my struggle. Indeed, I can honestly say to myself that I am running the race and running it well. I have not lost the faith given to me by my grandfather and I can continue his legacy of service to others. Now I'm able to be the father that I longed to have, and support my wife with an attentive, open heart. I crave a sense of deep, honest connection with other people and I long to listen to the struggles of others, without judgment or inquisition. Their struggle is their struggle. There is no need to carry the burden of the world and "right" all wrongs. I no longer need to be perfect and there are more opportunities to fail than succeed. I embrace the challenge of life- to fall, get up, and keep moving forward.

As of today, I have been able to set goals toward recovery. I want to be spirit-led, strong, lean, and flexible in both mind and body. I want to connect with others in a deep, meaningful way. Instead of scouring over scientific literature for the answers to my questions, I seek the Spirit that was placed in me to guide my life. I want to serve others to continue the legacy of my grandfather. I meditate, I pray, I journal, and I wait. I fight the urge to seek out solutions to problems that don't even exist. I live in the moment. I have a vision that will take years to complete. I'm not focused on the goal of achievement; I'm interested in the depth of the relationships I can make along this path. I want to live a life of meaning, faith, and love. Love for my family, my friends, and others. Love for my God.

What have I learned? I've learned that we must process our emotions in a healthy way. Journaling, meditation, prayer, and strengthening my connection to others has allowed me to become a light to the world. There is no prescriptive solution and each person must find his or her own path. In order to be different, you must do different. If you are tired of the same result, try something new. When you feel overwhelmed, ask for help. Call a friend and have a support network. We were never intended to be isolated and live this life alone. Finally, learn to embrace your struggle. You are being forged into a warrior.

Greg's Story: A Warrior's Mindset

I grew up in a rough area nicknamed Criminal Hill. I was the youngest kid on my street which meant groups of older street kids would surround me, beat me up, and try to intimidate me daily. I hated being small and weak, I hated not being able to walk tall, I hated being pushed around, but I didn't know how to change it.

Then as an eight-year-old boy, a new television series began. It was named "Kung Fu" and I was hooked from the start. Each Tuesday night I would sit on the edge of my parents' bed watching this series. I remember being amazed at how such a slender, peaceful man could so effortlessly disable and disarm any number of assailants; just thinking about having that ability was exhilarating and from that point on I wanted to be a martial arts master.

One thing I have learned in my life is you can kick a dog so many times, and it will eventually die - or it will bite you. I was determined to be the dog that bit back. Even though I had always feared fighting, I hounded my parents to enroll me in martial arts. I immersed myself in weight training along with the study of martial arts and the history of Budo. Very soon my bedroom walls were coated in images of karate masters from across the world.

This became the catalyst for me to dream.

From that point on, whenever the local kids would beat me and bully me all I would ever say to them was, "One day you'll pay." They used to feign fear before breaking into roars of laughter.

Over the coming years things started to change, on top of my martial arts I had taken up weight training, and now I was also getting strong. Then one day it happened, the street kids tried their games on me again, but this time I was prepared. I don't want to go into detail about the incident that followed, but let's just say they left me alone after that day. I walked home, looked in the mirror and smiled. I had become a different person. No longer the target, no longer the brunt of the jokes or beatings. I was a true martial artist.

Forty years later, I am a true Sensei with my own traditional Okinawan Karate School, my own students, and a great deal of pride for what I instill in them. However, it was what the journey to mastery taught me that changed my life. It allowed me to succeed on the world stage in a variety of arenas outside of the martial arts, including bodybuilding, movies and now speaking.

The warrior's mindset taught me to fight through the hard times and to fight back. Sometimes I could see the foes, and other times I fought to overcome severe bouts of depression, including life-ending thoughts.

Today I fight to be a voice and advocate in the world of suicide prevention.

One of my life endeavors was to become a film director. Over a fifteen-year period and completely uneducated in the field, I managed to teach myself enough skills by trial and error that my career made it all the way to Hollywood.

I was chosen to be the principal Fight Choreographer and Weapons Specialist for the film Mad Max Fury Road. My role included dreaming up and designing all the fighting and gunfighting action pieces for the film, which when you think about it is pretty much the entire film.

This was one of the most arduous tasks I have ever had to complete. Incredibly, this was my first job as a fight choreographer, and it was on the largest live-action film ever made. There was to be one major obstacle I had to deal with to get the job done: politics. There was a great deal of animosity amongst some of the department heads and a few departments in general which made the process rough. I had specific people working against me from the very start, and this continued throughout the project. Nevertheless, the fight team poured everything we had into this movie to bring it to life.

Then, just as we were about to do the final filming, budget issues intensified. One day, the studio came in, and with the single stroke of a pen, we were stopped.

On my birthday a few weeks later, I started to wonder when we were heading back to finish the film. So, I called our producer to be confronted with the news that we weren't. I nearly fell over. We returned home to be hit with a massive tax bill, no work, and no prospects. Now we were in damage control.

We searched for film opportunities but there was nothing. I scoured for work options and any viable way to bringing in a decent level of income, but still there was nothing. I had to face the facts that it was the Christmas break, and no one was working.

I thought I had a block of time to get a new position, but that quickly vanished when I was hit with a large tax bill. In a flash it had become clear that if I didn't get some work soon then there was a very sobering reality of losing our home. The money was going out, but little was coming in.

Then one day a friend approached me and said, "I might be able to find you work on our construction site in the city if you're interested." I said, "If there's any work I will take it." He said, "It's a rotten job, but money's money."

So, I went in. After the first meeting I found myself in a bright orange protective suit, thick gloves, gas mask, goggles, and a hard hat.

Like a flock of sheep, we were herded down a long dirt pathway to a place known to all that worked there as "The Hole." I had found out at the induction that this was a high dangerous site. It was the middle of summer and, regardless of the work, we had to continually wear this apparel. Now don't get me wrong, I love hard physical work, getting in amongst it and striving with a team, but my first three months weren't exactly like that. I literally spent my first three months inside what I named "the hole inside The Hole." It was a mud-based elevator shaft around 10 meters below ground, scraping mud and hard dirt from the steel sheet pile walls with a shovel.

It was mentally debilitating. I had gone from working with Hollywood A-list actors, running large teams of film professionals, designing, and choreographing major combat action sequences, to being stuck in knee-deep mud scraping dirt from walls for over sixty hours a week. Every cent I earned went to pay bills as we fought to keep the house.

Working in construction showed me why the industry has so many suicides. The workers on this rat-wheel all work massive hours, nearly every day of every week all year with nothing to show for it. Why? Many of them have gambling debts, are on their third or fourth marriage, separated, or suffer from drug and alcohol addictions. They use drugs or alcohol as a form of escape from the endless void that is work. I know firsthand, as it almost took me to the point of ending my life. I felt ashamed, like I had let everybody down.

I thought, "What have I done to deserve this? How did it all go so wrong?" On top of this I was becoming a bad father. I had no energy to spend any quality time with my kids, and when I did, I was horrible to be around. Life in our home was becoming miserable. This downward spiral kept on going.

Over the coming months I was descending to a very dark place in my mind. I contemplated all kinds of things. After a year, I was in a very poor mental headspace. I got to the point where I didn't think I could go on. You see, this entire place reminded me of a prison. We all wore orange overalls, gas masks, and hardhats. Most of us were long-termers and most of us hated it. I was trying to find anything I could grasp onto in order to survive this ordeal, but I was running out of options.

It's amazing how in a time of crisis the smallest things can become the most important.

Fast-forward to my birthday, January 9, 2014. I had come to absolutely hate myself. How could I have allowed my life to come to this? I had become the failure I never wanted to be. I got up quietly, entered my children's room, and gently sat on the bed. I sat there for a while just staring at their innocent faces as they slept. I reached out and touched them both, not knowing if I would ever come home to see them again. I grabbed my hardhat from the corner, and as I was about to leave, my son opened his eyes and whispered to me, "Love you, Daddy."

It stopped me in my tracks.

I was in a bad headspace, but my family needed me, and for us to make it through this I would have to make some serious life changes. I knew how much mental pain and depression I was suffering, but I also knew the pain that the many suicides I had endured had brought to my life, and I didn't want my family to suffer from that demon as I had.

I walked into work a little late that day. A co-worker walked past me. He headed to the decontamination chamber, took off all his protective gear, and headed up around 14 flights of stairs to the top of the structure. I didn't know he was in trouble. I didn't think to look up as he climbed to the edge of the scaffolding. I was fighting through my own nightmare, oblivious to the pain of others.

Oblivious until WHAM! He slammed to the ground beside us. His life was causing him too much mental pain, and he couldn't take it anymore. That day he succumbed to the pain and took his life.

Everybody rushed in to help try and save him, but it was too late; he was gone. The workers were completely devastated. I called MATES in Construction, who are a suicide charity and had been very active on the site. I said, "We've just had an incident. Someone has lost their life. You need to get counselors down here now, as we're going to need you." Very quickly the site was evacuated and all the workers who had witnessed this unfortunate and incredibly sad event headed to the meeting rooms whilst the police arrived to perform an investigation. I was questioned along with several other colleagues about what had happened.

I returned to the meeting rooms to see all these big tough guys just sitting there silently, glassy eyed, not knowing what to say or do. That was the point I decided enough was enough. So I stood up and spoke to them about life and how quickly things can compound and cascade into the abyss of unknown, which can lead to depression and suicide.

I told them of my life experiences but never told them just how close I had been to the edge. I said that we should be the worksite where guys have the guts to speak about their issues, so together we can help each other find a solution. I finished by saying, "This is a shit sandwich. We never want to go through this again, so if anyone else here is feeling the same way, you come and see me when I'm finished. I will walk you to help myself!" When I was done and the room cleared, six men came up to me saying that they had been having similar thoughts of suicide.

So I walked with them all to get them the help they needed.

That day was an awakening to me, I truly feel like we lost one life, but saved seven: those six blokes and me. That was the moment I knew I had something of value to speak of, and it had come to me at the lowest point in my life.

It was then and there I decided to be a speaker. I wanted to help people find their vision again, learn from their mistakes and better their lives. To do this I knew I had to turn my entire life around. So I began. During my breaks, I started writing speeches, began listening to inspirational speakers on my phone whilst I was shoveling and started practicing at nights.

Today I am a national ambassador for Australia's Lifeline and Suicide Prevention Australia. It's why I speak wherever and whenever I can to help people find hope, and it's why I smile each day when I wake, as I work to bring hope and inspiration to all that I meet.

I realized there was fire inside me. I was bettering myself for something much larger than external appreciation; I was doing this to save lives. Since that day, when I discovered the power my words could have on another human life, I have wanted to be the agent of change. I want to be the voice for the eleven friends, and my loving Aunty, whom I lost to depression and suicide.

Govan's Story: Do You See Holes in Your Hands?

I thought I grew up in the normal All-American Family: a mother, a father, and two kids. My dad was a Pennsylvania State Trooper, and my mom was a housewife. I was the oldest, and my brother Michael and I were only 11 months apart. Our parents brought us up in a very strict household. Church and school were always in the forefront while growing up, and I even thought about becoming a priest. More than anything, family always came first. I can remember my dad saying to my brother and me: ALWAYS protect each other; "If one brother gets in a fight, then the other brother better be there to fight also."

Life was going pretty great for me. I was a lifeguard during the summers at a public pool starting when I was 15. I LOVED that job: being out in the sun, especially with all the girls. Girls, girls... that was the end of the priest-vocation thoughts.

The perfect picture of "family" took a major hit when my mom and dad separated in

September 1979. I could count on one hand the times I had heard them fight, and it usually wasn't anything serious, or so I thought.

I can also remember taking some anger out on my brother. He seemed to be on my dad's side, and I was on my mom's side. There would be arguments and punching battles between us on and off for a few months.

Then Michael told me one day while we were driving around doing errands that he was thinking about killing himself. It was in November '79. I was in shock and didn't know what to say. I probably said something like, "Why would you want to do that?"

Michael didn't say anything else about it. He just stared out the car window.

I went home and told my dad. Dad immediately talked to Michael and told me about an hour later that Michael would be okay. I never doubted that after he told me.

In January 1980, I had my FIRST girlfriend, Christine. I was excited for this new change in my life, especially after my mom and dad's separation. Being 17 and finally having a girl-friend was just fantastic. I was very shy and kept everything inside for pretty much all my life, but I saw that changing with Christine.

Then on January 30, 1980, I walked home from school and went into my house and saw Michael lying on the floor with a small pool of blood around his head.

Then I saw the gun.

I did see him breathing and thought, "Thank God." I ran out of the house and down the street to my best friend's house. I remember pounding at the door and half-collapsing on their porch saying over and over again, "Michael shot himself!"

I don't remember who came out first, but I know my friend John and his dad just started running to my house. I followed them but slowed up because I knew what I was going back to. I got to the doorway and I felt an imaginary barrier keeping me out. I kept on hearing John's dad saying, "Michael, Michael!" Before I knew it, a few ambulances arrived.

Then I saw my dad get out of an unmarked police car and go inside.

I remember an EMT taking my blood pressure. I was just numb and in shock. Then I went to my friend's house and waited for my dad to come back.

An hour later my dad walked through the door and just looked at me. He didn't have to say a word, as I knew what he was going to tell me. Michael had died. I just remembered sobbing and wailing. This couldn't be happening. My immediate thought was that THIS IS ALL MY FAULT! He told me that he wanted to kill himself, and I didn't protect him.

After the funeral, the only thing that I wanted to do was see Christine. I went over to her house not knowing what she or her family would say. I walked in the house and she gave me a hug. I sat down in their living room and her dad ordered everyone out of the room and said that he wanted to talk to me alone. After they left the room, he just looked at me and said, "Govan, I am so sorry for what happened. If there is anything that I can do for you, just let me know. I promise that I will be here for you no matter what."

I felt so comforted by what he said. Part of me thought he was just being nice, but I wanted so much to believe what he was telling me. He was the ONLY person who had ever "talked" to me about Michael and gave me permission to talk about if I wanted to.

For the next nine months, I was kept afloat by Christine and her family. Her family treated me like I was a part of their family. I didn't really care about anything else. I didn't care about school or college. The only source of happiness that I had was spending time with Christine. And then Christine broke up with me. I never blamed her, as I became very possessive while we were dating because I just thought I couldn't lose her, too. I didn't see what I was doing to her. Well, that was the trifecta: my parents separating, Michael dying, and Christine breaking up with me.

Everything in me fell apart. I was just barely 18.

For the next few years I just "hung on" in life. I didn't do well in school and didn't care. I just remember crying a lot and feeling very alone.

In 1983, I entered the Pennsylvania State Police Academy, following in my dad's footsteps to become a Trooper myself. I loved being a Trooper - great job, good money, and it gave me confidence in myself that I didn't have before.

In 1991, I started dating a girl named JoAnn. JoAnn was a pharmacist, but what I liked about JoAnn was her honesty and her smile. In the first few weeks of dating, JoAnn told me that she had attempted suicide when she was 18. She told me that she was still taking medication and seeing a therapist from time to time. Things didn't work out after a few months, but we still stayed in touch. JoAnn called me one night about a year later and told me she was thinking about suicide. I talked to her for over four hours on the phone. I asked her if she was safe, and she told me she was at her parents' house and that they were talking care of her. As we were getting off the phone, I asked her if she was still thinking about suicide, and she said no and that she would be okay. I told her that I would always love her and be there for her, and she said the same thing back to me. The next day, I got a phone call from her friend telling me that JoAnn had killed herself.

I FAILED AGAIN.

I went into GUILT mode again. I remember at her service thinking that everyone was looking at me because I failed her. I thought, "What the FUCK am I doing wrong in life, and how am I failing everyone around me?"

Through several years, I found myself growing in confidence at work but failing at the relationships in my life, never talking about Michael or JoAnn. I always ended up getting involved in relationships that were not good for me. At one point, I was engaged to someone who threatened to kill herself if I broke-up with her; only to find out that she told me that so I would stay with her. But the straw that broke the proverbial camel's back was another relationship that just totally made me fall apart. She lied, she cheated, and I still wanted her back. That relationship became so toxic and heartbreaking to the point where I was asking myself and God, "Why am I here, what purpose do I have in life?" During that time, I remember having a work meeting with two psychologists over lunch and suddenly starting to cry in the middle of lunch. State Troopers DO NOT CRY, especially in front of others! They asked what was wrong, and I told them that my girlfriend had just left me. They suggested that I should talk to someone. It was the first time in my life I knew I needed someone professional to speak with.

I started to see the psychologist in January 2000 and stayed with her several years. She became a necessity for me for the next few months after that relationship ended. She just let me talk and talk about Michael and JoAnn. After a few years, I finally had a breakthrough as to why I was feeling the way I did about myself. She asked me one day in a session to 'look at the palms of your hands' and then to turn them over. She asked, "Do you see holes in them?" I said no, but after a few seconds it dawned on me exactly what she meant, and I started to cry. I realized at that moment that I was not Christ, I was not responsible for saving my brother, or JoAnn, for saving those relationships that weren't good for me, or for saving the entire world for that matter. She made me say those thoughts out loud. That was the epiphany and breakthrough that I needed. This was a huge healing- and turning-point in my life and one the that I needed to hear.

The highlight of my work in the Pennsylvania State Police was overseeing our Peer Support Program for the last 12 years of my career. That position allowed me to help others with job, life, and personal problems, even helping those who were considering suicide. There was, and is, no greater reward than knowing that the people I helped who were considering suicide are still alive today! My Peer Support training showed me that LISTENING is the best way to help others. Not only did I learn listening techniques from my training in Peer Support, but I knew the benefit of experiencing them firsthand from working with my psychologist.

I retired from the State Police in 2012 after 29 years, and now am a Suicide Prevention Advocate. I am currently Executive Director and Chair of our Board of Directors for Prevent Suicide Pennsylvania. I am helped by helping other people.

Remember Christine's Dad? He kept his promise until the day he died. I heard from him once or twice every year from 1980 on asking me how I was doing and inviting me over to dinner, always saying, "Why don't you come over more often?" He kept his promise to me for over 30 years; he cared about me, and more importantly, he listened to me. He was my second dad.

Thoreau said that most men lead lives of quiet desperation, but what I have learned in life is that most people - including all those who struggle - lead quiet lives of heroism, perseverance, and integrity.

BUILDING YOUR MENTAL MECHANIC'S TOOLBOX

PART 2

TOOL #3: Take a Head Inspection

Right now, in the privacy of your own phone or computer, you can take one of these mental health screenings to see how you're doing on things like depression, anxiety, anger, and substance use:

- Man Therapy 20-Point Head Inspection: www.ManTherapy.org

- Mental Health America Screening Tools: https://screening.mental-healthamerica.net/screening-tools

- Help Yourself. Help Others: https://helpyourselfhelpothers.org/

TOOL #4: Organize a Local Gatekeeper Training for Your Community

Research each of these to see which one is the best fit for your community based on time, cost, and scope:

- QPR (Question, Persuade, Refer): https://qprinstitute.com/

- safeTALK: https://www.livingworks.net/safetalk

- Talk Saves Lives: https://afsp.org/our-work/education/talk-saves-lives-introduction-suicide-prevention/

- Mental Health First Aid: https://www.mentalhealthfirstaid.org/

TOOL #5: Hazard Mitigation Plan for the Highway of Life

The best way to deal with the hazards of stress is to develop a plan to handle them before they arrive. None of us gets through our life's journey without hardship, so this exercise is designed to help you figure out what you are going to do when hazards like break-ups, layoffs, illnesses, and other issues come your way.

- **HOPE BOX:** What are your reasons for living? What brings you joy and meaning? [maybe collect pictures or mementos of these things and put them in a box; when you are stressed, pull them out to remind you of the bigger picture].

- **TOUCHSTONE BACK ON YOUR RESILIENCE:** What have you done before to cope when you were overwhelmed? What calms you down and gets you focused on the things that matter?

- **WHAT INTERRUPTS YOU WHEN YOU ARE DRIVING IN CIRCLES?** What things take your mind off your problems? What distracts you when you find yourself obsessing about negative things?

- **BUILD NEW COPING SKILLS:** Research and practice the emotional and interpersonal skills offered in DBT. Here are some additional resources to get more information:

> www.NowMattersNow.org

> McKay, M., Wood, J. & Brantly, J. (2007). The Dialectical Behavior Therapy Skills Workbook: Practical DBT Exercises for Learning Mindfulness, Interpersonal Effectiveness, Emotion Regulation & Distress Tolerance (A New Harbinger Self-Help Workbook).

Other Resources - take notes of other resources or coping skills you find:

TOOL #6: Explore Formal Peer Support Options

This assignment will take some research on your part, as access to in-person peer support varies greatly by region. Nevertheless, here are a few options to get you started:

- Search 12-Step Recovery programs related to your compulsive or addictive behavior. These peer-facilitated groups are always free and many now have phone and online access.

- Search the Depression/Bipolar Support Alliance or "peer support groups for _____"

- Search "Peer Warm Lines" — these will usually connect you to well-trained peer supporters

- Check out iRel8.org - an online, global, anonymous social network for mental wellness that brings people together in a safe community, 24/7, to provide a safe forum for people to help and heal each other.

Questions to ask as you are deciding whether a peer support program is a good fit for you:

- Where/when does the group meet? If not a group - how often might I expect to connect with an individual peer supporter?

- Is the group accepting new members and what are the criteria to join? Are there costs?

- How many people are involved in this peer support program?

- How are lead peer supporters selected, trained, and supervised?

- Is the program affiliated with any organizations or programs? Do you want a faith-based component?

- Does the program do anything to protect the confidentiality of its members? What, if anything, gets documented?

- If there are meetings, what does a typical meeting look like? How are new members oriented?

Sometimes, as with most everything in life, finding a good fit can be a bit of a trial-and-error process. If you decide to take part in a formal peer support program, reflect on how it's going by asking:

- Do I feel supported?

- Do I have opportunities to learn, give, and receive?

- Do I feel safe to address uncomfortable feelings or conflict when they arise?

- Does this feel right for me?

BREAKDOWN, REPAIR & OVERHAUL

CHAPTER 4: BREAKDOWN, REPAIR & OVERHAUL

So, you've deferred all routine maintenance. You've haven't changed the oil, topped off the fluids, flushed the radiator, replaced the air filter, serviced the transmission, changed out the timing belt, rotated, balanced and kept proper pressure in the tires, replaced the worn-out brake pads, or renewed your AAA membership. You wonder why you find your-self stranded on the side of the road, in the middle of nowhere, with a car whose engine has overheated or blown, or transmission is trashed, or brakes have failed, or tire has gone flat, or a combination of any of those, with no one you can call to tow it to the nearest repair facility. Who'd'a thunk?

If you treated your body and your brain the same way, chances are you'd find yourself broken down, stranded and alone as well. This section of the book helps us figure out how to deal with crisis; how to see crisis as opportunity. As John F. Kennedy said, "When written in Chinese, the word 'crisis' is composed of two characters. One represents danger and the other represents opportunity." While he was wrong about the Chinese characters, the idea that crisis is composed of both danger and opportunity still holds true.

What Does Crisis Mean?

A loss of power and control

Who among us hasn't had the power steering pump fail, and found ourselves trying to control 3000 pounds of Detroit steel with brute force? Not a day at the beach...

This is why crises are so overwhelming and demand our attention. The emotions we experience during a crisis are visceral and immediate. The thoughts we have are negative and urgent because our brains want us to take action to solve the problem, to survive. When we see these crises as a threat to our life, we react. We get mobilized to fight, flee, or freeze.

If we see the threat of crisis as a challenge AND an opportunity, however, we can cultivate a can-do mindset and live through it. In contrast to the threat reaction which ignites fear, frustration, and hopelessness, the challenge mindset spurs inspiration and determination to tackle the crisis head-on.[29] Fear can be a mind killer. Serious martial arts students learn techniques so that when faced with a threat their pulse rate actually drops and their breathing slows. They relax to prepare for whatever comes next rather than anticipating something they might imagine will be awful. They often adopt what's called a 'soft focus,' meaning rather than focus on the face or the hands of the person who appears to be threatening them, they soften their focus to take in the other person from head to toe. Not anticipating trouble - simply being prepared for whatever comes next.

A threat to your identity

Yes, it's your vehicle, and yes, you intended to pay that car payment, but now the bank is repossessing it. You were so proud to drive around town with it, and now you watch it being towed away.

Because many men pride themselves as being "The Big Wheel" (successful), "The Sturdy Oak" (self-reliant and confident), and "The Leader" (being in charge at all times) crises can shatter these core beliefs and cast men into a downward spiral of self-doubt.

Immobilization

You forgot to renew your registration and you aren't supposed to drive again until you've renewed it and delivered proof to the DMV to get your driving privileges back. Now you're stuck at home.

In the first stages of responding to a crisis, you may find yourself in shock. Disbelief and what psychologists call "emotional numbing" are common. You may second-guess all your decisions. At the grocery store, should I have chosen paper over plastic? This phase is often very unnerving for a man who used to pride himself on his decisiveness.

Escalation

You saw the guy in the truck ahead of you. You didn't mean to rear end him, but the brakes you'd been meaning to replace finally went soft and since, unlike Fred Flintstone, you couldn't just employ your big feet, and because your power steering pump was out you couldn't swerve the car away, you hit him.

Often crises seem to hit us like a domino effect. A work crisis can worsen a health crisis. A financial crisis can lead to a marital crisis. Sometimes our poor coping strategies to deal with the uncomfortable feelings associated with the crisis lead to more crises – like DUIs, fights, and illegal activities. Then men find themselves facing legal issues on top of everything else and hurting people they never intended to hurt.

Involuntary Intervention

You knew you shouldn't drink and drive. You were only going to have a couple of beers, and really, it's not that far home, you've driven it a million times! What could go wrong? What went wrong was you wound up in the hospital, in detox, with a DUI.

When your behavior is at risk of hurting others or yourself, society has deemed it necessary to remove some of your civil rights until you can get yourself back on the right track. This may mean having your wages garnished, being hospitalized involuntarily, or having your driver's license suspended.

Hopelessness

You have no car, because you have no license. And once you get it back, because of the DUI you won't be able to afford the insurance, so you roll the dice and drive without insurance. Then you hit someone; both cars are totaled. With no insurance, there's no money to fix your car or to pay for the other guy's car - or his medical bills - so his insurance company pays to fix his car and pays his medical bills, and you learn a new word: subrogation. It's what his insurance company does to you. They come to collect the money they spent on their insured that you hit. You don't have insurance, so they sue, win, and take your house, and anything else of value that you own. And you thought you needed a drink before!

These types of escalating problems often lead men to feel a deep despair and hopelessness. "How will I ever climb out of this hole? These problems just seem too big to solve!" Sometimes the wiring of our depressed brain can turn up the volume on this hopelessness and make things seem worse than they actually are.

The trap of hopelessness is that men can start to get stuck in extreme all-or-nothing thoughts that make the problems worse:

- I will never be able to climb out of this hole.

- No one can help me.

- My problems are too big to solve.

- I give up.

- My future will always be dark.

- I will never be happy again.

Profound Isolation

When you have no form of transportation, you can often feel like a burden to friends and family from whom you must beg rides. Instead, you just keep to yourself.

During crises we need social support more than any other time, but for many men the inclination is to pull away. Whether it's due to shame or not feeling like they should ask for help, many men go into 'machismo mode' – "I don't need anyone. I can do this all on my own." This 'lone wolf' syndrome may protect you from the initial scary experiences of being vulnerable, but in the long run, it leaves you lonely and more at risk for depression and suicide. There is a reason wolves travel in packs: they understand that being a lone wolf exposes you to all sorts of problems and dangers.

Meet the Mental Mechanics for System Breakdown, Repair, and Overhaul

So, let's read on to see what other men have done to reverse this downward spiral of events.

Mike's Story: The Flip of a Switch; A Life Plan Derailed

Finding the Purpose of a Train Wreck

On July 19, 2011, my life ended.

At the time, I was a 27-year-old train conductor in Montana; a career that can be very demanding but allowed me to provide a quality of life for my family that even my college education could not afford. People would sometimes ask me if I got bored intellectually, as if the career were not stimulating enough. I offset the negatives of the career by focusing on the positives like the one-on-one environment of the cab. I'd have fascinating conversations with co-workers - former teachers, geologists, computer designers, investors, farmers, land-scapers, and many other types of professions that had all joined the profession in hopes of being able to provide a good lifestyle. Being an outdoorsy person, working on the rail gave me a mobile office and front row seat through some of the most scenic landscape on Earth.

In hindsight, I had a pretty damn good life and one that seems almost like a dream teas-ing me with thoughts of what could have been. My college experience included scholarships for football and wrestling. Professionally, even though I had seen career opportunities waver through grant funding cuts and furloughs, I had always been fiscally responsible and sound. A man who's currently a judge once told me I had done a fine job of marrying 'above myself.' My daughter, 6 months old at the time, was the perfect baby, rarely ever crying and sporting a gorgeous smile. I'm not sure I could have imagined a happier vision for myself.

Then, one fateful day, my dream turned into a nightmare. Onboard a freight train in dark territory my engineer and I rounded a corner to see a train parked in the siding, a siding that we were erroneously lined into. My train was over a mile long and over ten thousand tons, and the emergency brake lever flopped down with a pathetic limpness after I dumped the air. I knew I was going to die, and I felt terrible for that six-month-old that was going to grow up without her father. There was an awkward moment of futility that occurred, when the realization that I had no control almost had a paralytic effect. It's wasn't even necessarily all fear, but rather knowing that no action I could take would change the fact that I was going to die. Eventually as the sound of my engineer's voice fought through that moment of shock, I followed his lead and resigned to my deathbed on the dusty floor of the locomotive cab. I laid there for what felt like an eternity - but was only seconds - feeling a terrible guilt for leaving an infant fatherless.

It's hard to describe how long seconds become in a moment like that. Time crawls by so much so that I started to un-tuck myself from the fetal position in an attempt to look around and see if, somehow, we had averted disaster. In that moment I felt the one thing that only a railroader could understand: I felt the violent sway of our engine as we hit a 10-mph turnout at over 30 mph. That moment the true definition of terror was revealed to me. That moment was confirmation that, indeed, we were going to collide with that train in the siding. Even after the time that has passed since that endless moment, it is the one I don't discuss in a crowd, I don't describe to friends, and I don't try to 'feel.'

As I sit here typing this, I still believe that, in some sense, part of me did die when my train hit that other train. What I went through after that day, for a long period of time, I can only describe as Hell on Earth. A lot of my ideas of what it meant to be a man, a father, and a husband were no longer ideals I could identify with myself. Thoughts like: "What kind of man has panic attacks?" "How can I provide for my family now?" "What good am I?" "I can't even lift the jug onto the water cooler" were predominant and destroying my definition of my own identity. I was experiencing panic attacks, depression, and feelings of shame. The physical limitations and pain, as a result of the extensive damage done to my back, did not help my mental status.

Inevitably the foundations of my life crumbled. After a year of treatment, I was unable to safely perform work for the railroad, my wife asked for a divorce, and at 28 years old I underwent my first back surgery. After the surgery, lying in agony in my father's basement, I felt like a monumental burden, a disappointment, a failure, and a waste not even worthy of breathing. I had been a very independent and bright young man who took pride in always being able to find a solution to whatever problems life presented; at this point though, I had no solutions. A question crept into my mind:

"Why?"

Why deal with the pain and the agony that was my existence at the time? My life had become too painful to endure and ending it seem like the only way to stop the pain. As I brought my pistol up to the side of my head, just like when I was facing that parked train in the siding, I waited for impact and my inevitable nonexistence, but my thoughts focused on that little girl who would grow up without her father. I have experienced some tremendous 'cries' in the past five years, but few have been similar to that one when I found a reason, a meaning, to keep fighting the pain. I cried thinking about how that would have affected her life, which meant that I was still worth something to someone.

After that realization of meaning - to be a father that didn't quit - I had a reason, I had purpose, and I had leverage against the pain. I still get choked up and experience a feeling of nausea when I think about the low point I was at that night.

I had sought counseling after the wreck and had been attending on a weekly basis, but it was in a session shortly after that low-point in my father's basement that I was able to find hope and figure out a path that would allow me to find an identity again. Even though I had been attending counseling, I struggled for over a year with trying to find an answer. My entire life plan had been wiped out in a matter of minutes, and I felt an unbelievable amount of pressure to try to come up with a new one. Asking for help can be a difficult thing for anyone, especially working-age men. I believe the only reason I did is because I had heard this message so many times in my prior career – ask for help. For a short period, I had even been a spokesman at the state level for my county's mental health committee but had never honestly thought about being a consumer of mental health services. It's not always easy finding a reason to go on, but this has made an enormous difference and allowed me to expand my answer to that simple question, "Why?" Every time I hear some form of the word 'Dad' come from my daughter's mouth I remember why.

Another thing that has helped keep me going is an unrelenting family to whom I do not give enough credit.

"Do something, anything, to not be trapped in the pit of despair," my father urged as he kept forcing me to do simple housework and attend physical therapy.

I hated him for it initially. I was in so much physical and mental pain. Though I am limited compared to the athlete I once was, my commitment to physical therapy broke up that cycle of despair. My brothers dragged me out to fish and never complained about the expenses. The first time I caught a fish after the wreck I cried because of the intense burning sensation it caused in my back; that was humbling. I had surgery in the winter, and my brothers dragged me back out in the spring to get me out of the house and doing something I had enjoyed. Working out or fishing with my daughter still to this day reminds me of how thankful I am to be here and how far I have come.

Honestly, I've never wanted to run from anything in my life the way I want to run away from the rail industry. However, I told a great man that people in this industry need advocates, that those coworkers who shared their knowledge and amazing stories with me were still out there working in an unforgiving industry with harsh psychological conditions, along with many others like them. That great man agreed that trainmen need advocates and asked me what I was going to do about it. At the time of this discussion, I had been seeking advice on a research paper for my graduate degree. That research was supposed to be on changing the mental health culture of a vocational field in which we had knowledge. With his encouragement, I have shared the ideas in that paper with other mental health experts and potential agents of change in the industry. My desire is that sharing my ideas and experiences on what it's like to be suffering and to be battling the various hurdles to recovery in the industry will help reduce and prevent the future suffering of other railroaders. After years of physical therapy, counseling, and the successful pursuit of a master's degree in counseling, I would like to help others to find their 'Why?' In this process of helping others, I too will benefit from a sense of purpose and greater meaning by using my experience of pain and suffering to help others with their own.

"He who has a Why to live can bear almost any How." (Friedrich Nietzsche).

Ethan's Story: Breaking Out of the Cage

I was an athlete lost in years of depression with ongoing suicidal thoughts. These thoughts were hidden in secrecy from the world and overlooked because of my ability to play basketball. Life was clouded by self-medicating and addiction. Basketball was my love. Alcohol and drugs my warm comforting mistress. My daily drinking, weed smoking, pill popping lifestyle took control.

Drinking to die most nights was my goal, instead of trying to stay sober and get my act together to play college basketball. My cycle of addiction took me to five college basketball programs in three states, only to chew me up and spit me out. My internal struggle battling demons was a daily routine. My depression and addiction not only caused harm to me and my family, but it also caused indescribable pain to a family I didn't even know.

In 2003, my life was about to drastically change.

Close your eyes as tight as you can. So tight that your eyes begin to tear. During this process visualize and imagine opening those eyes to a dark hospital room. Shades covering windows where only the slightest evening light embraces the darkness. I opened my eyes to this very moment, utterly confused and unaware of why and how I ended up in the hospital. A dark fog clouded my thoughts before a nurse entered the room. An uneasy feeling was in the air, not knowing if this was reality or a nightmare. Shortly after, a second nurse enters the room. Slowly opening my dried lips, I whisper out, "Why am I here?" with hesitation she says, "You drove drunk and killed somebody last night."

A deadly silence vibrated the room. Tears began to fall as the words finally began to sink in. "What did I just do? Was this a nightmare?" These were the only thoughts screaming in my head.

After hours of crying and staring at a blank wall, I remember thinking to myself that I wanted to die. I was going to kill myself. I couldn't live knowing what I did. Then I quickly thought about fleeing the country; I wasn't handcuffed, and I had friends in other countries. Images of my brothers and parents appeared, sending me to tears, thinking, "I can't leave them." Finally, a wave of something unexplainable seemed to enter my thoughts. Something told me to handle my responsibilities and take full accountability for what I had done. Prior to this moment I had no religious or spiritual thought or belief. At that moment, I believe God in some manner told me to live and handle this horrendous situation and not take the easy way out. From that moment in time, that exact moment, something changed in me.

The next eight months of my life were on bond. Living at home after the accident was the darkest and scariest time in my life. All I could think about was the man I killed. During this time doctors and psychiatrists were prescribing me more pills than a pharmacy. These eight months were a prescription-pill-filled emotionless void. Countless days and nights were filled with a desire to take my own life, but I lacked the energy to make an attempt because of all of the Seroquel, Ambien, Lexapro, Wellbutrin, Lithium, and a sprinkle of Clonazepam they had added to my diet. I was a walking zombie with blood flowing in my veins and a non-functioning vegetative brain in my skull.

Court came, and my punishment was inevitable. The judge slammed the gavel and sentenced me to 10 years of Department of Corrections with a five-year parole sentence. I pleaded guilty to a DUI vehicular homicide. County jail was my first stop before being sent to the Diagnostic Reporting Department of Corrections (DRDC) prison. Sitting in the van entering multiple gates, surrounded by layers and layers of razor wire was a moment I would never forget. Changes were coming.

My first six weeks of prison were in 23-hour lockdown. Locked in a six-by-nine cell with nothing but brick walls, a mattress pad, metal desk, and a silver toilet connected to a sink and mirror. All day long I would ask myself, "Was this really happening to me? Was I really an inmate of the Department of Corrections? Was I locked up with criminals, drug dealers, armed robbers and even killers?" Yes, I was. This was my reality. I deserved to be in prison. Within that confined brick-walled cell, I had to quickly shift my mindset. I would show no weakness, no depression, no emotions. I was in prison with grown men who saw weakness as an opportunity. All the depressive, suicidal thoughts I had after the accident had to be bottled up, locked deep inside and internalized. I couldn't let anybody see how much I was hurting.

During those six weeks of isolation I made up in my mind that I was going to use this prison sentence to build, construct, and strengthen a new and improved better me. I was going to read, write, and workout every hour of everyday. I was going to strengthen my body and mind. I would prepare for whatever obstacles I was going to face. I read over 50 books in six weeks and did over 1,000 push-ups per day. I was determined to be the best individual when I was released and free. I knew nobody was going to stop me from what I was going to achieve or obtain because I was determined and filled with desire.

After the month and a half of grueling isolation inside that cage, I was moved into a new phase of DRDC. Now I had to learn how to adapt to a six-by-nine cell, with a roommate, or 'celly.' This was extremely difficult and extremely scary. I had at least ten cellmates in the span of a couple of months.

Imagine being stuck inside a broom closet 22 hrs. per day, every day, with a man that robbed, dealt drugs, beat or killed others. One of my cellmates who had been stabbed or 'shanked' at another prison showed me the scars and worried me at night when I closed my eyes. We had no TV to watch, only books, one desk and notepads for both inmates to use 22 hours a day. We lived together in this tiny brick-encased cage that was similar in size to some of the cages you see at a zoo. Yes, imagine the clear glass animal enclosures that people can watch the lions, tigers, or gorillas up close, with the sign saying, "Do not touch the glass." As an inmate, you are nothing but a caged animal with a DOC number. You aren't a human being to most of the correctional officers, just a convict with a number. It's easy to understand where this thought process comes from. You cannot trust anybody.

Nearly three years of my life was spent incarcerated in prison. My time was easy com-pared to most. I took every opportunity that the DOC gave me to better myself. One of the best decisions I ever made was to volunteer for the DOC military boot camp program. The drill instructors were on-leave or retired ex-military. Some were Green Berets, Special Forces, and even Air Force. They were tough, bad dudes. Their goal was to break the inmates down to build them up. It was an awesome program. A dauntingly physical and mental challenge, only to make me better. I trained to be a Wildland Forest Firefighter and made the team. I took college courses and received numerous drug and alcohol certifications. Those programs gave me the motivation to make sure not to gamble and to stay away from prison politics and gang life.

With a new zest for life and desire to change, I took my new life out of prison and went back to college. I wanted to prove to the world that when you put your mind to something you can achieve anything. In a matter of five years I accomplished more goals than most can imagine. I earned two bachelor's degrees, three minors, and graduated magna cum laude and summa cum laude. On top of that, I earned the Entrepreneurship Student of the Year award for the business plan I developed in prison. Adding to that, I received the President's Award - the highest academic achievement you can earn at the University. Following that up, I went and earned my MBA and graduated magna cum laude as well. Even more amazing, I went back and played college basketball as an inmate of Colorado and coached the same team for three years after playing.

Today I speak around the country, telling my story of depression, addiction, and the horrific consequences of taking the life of an innocent man due to drinking and driving. My mission in life is to prevent others from ever drinking and driving. Taking the life of an innocent man will haunt me for the rest of my days. No matter how many degrees or thousands of students I influence and change, I can never bring his life back. That's a lifelong prison sentence I wish for nobody.

Sebastian's Story: Living in the Shadow of a Suicide

My father, Vernon Slovin, died by suicide when I was six years old, leaving my mom, little sister, and me in his wake. When my mom told me the news I remember feeling completely numb throughout my body. I didn't understand what happened at first. I didn't know what it meant that he took his own life. All I knew was that he was gone and he wasn't coming back.

In the weeks and months that followed, my mom grew more and more concerned about me. My sister was handling it very well, according to my mom's friend who was a psychologist. She was having major tantrums, which was interpreted as her "getting it all out." I was doing the opposite. Where before I had been incredibly talkative and had an insatiable curiosity, asking questions about everything, now I wasn't saying much at all and had pretty much shut down.

One night I lay in my bed trying to fall asleep and I could hear my mom crying from her room next door. I hated to hear her cry. It was the worst sound in the world to me. I plugged my ears. I put my head under the pillow, but I couldn't stop hearing it. I was overwhelmed with sadness and confusion. My dad wasn't coming back, and now my mom was crying every night. I felt helpless and lost. It seemed in that moment that the safest course of action was not to feel.

I put up walls and tried to insulate myself from a world which now seemed dark and foreign to me. Instead of lashing out or getting upset, I began to withdraw. I spent more and more time alone. I would stay in my room as much as I could. I would lie down on the floor, close my eyes, think about my dad and wish things would go back to the way they were.

To the best of my ability I blocked off, shut out, and pushed down the sadness, anger, and other emotions that were coming up. This was my plan for survival - I was not going to allow anything or anyone to hurt me again. I did what I needed to do to survive and, in the years immediately following my dad's suicide, this included a lot of isolation, avoidance, and running away.

As I got older and was able to more thoroughly comprehend the weight of my dad's suicide, things got worse. All sorts of feelings and questions around blame and shame started to come up. I found myself thinking about my dad and his suicide constantly, but the problem was I didn't feel like I could talk to anyone about it.

I wrote of this time in my book Ashes in the Ocean, "While I thought about my dad's suicide a great deal, growing up we [my family] very rarely spoke about the nature of his death. Sure, we alluded to it at times, tiptoeing around the proverbial elephant in the room, but we never spoke about it directly. For many years, we never even said the word "suicide." Suicide was like our version of Lord Voldemort or He Who Must Not Be Named in the world of Harry Potter. The word was something that loomed over us. It held great unspoken meaning and represented a whole world of guilt and shame by association. And, while we avoided using the word "suicide" or talking about it, it certainly had a deep impact on my mother, sister, and me. For much of my life, the stigma around suicide was lurking just beneath the surface. I was aware of it but couldn't see it clearly.

There were so many unanswered questions with my dad's suicide. And because of the stigma, these questions were often cloaked in guilt and shame. Why did this happen to my dad? Was there something about me that contributed to his death? Is there something wrong with me, with my family? Some of the stigma I felt around suicide certainly came from my own doing and thinking. And at the same time, a good portion of it came from the views of society and those around me.

We didn't talk about suicide at home, and one thing I learned early on was not to talk about it outside the home either. As I got older and my curiosity grew stronger, there were times when I did share with others what had happened to my dad. During those infrequent times that I talked about it, the responses I got certainly did not encourage me to share more."

For a long time I lived in the shadow of a suicide. The more I tried to avoid dealing with my past the worse things got and the more I felt controlled by it. It got to the point where I eventually felt destined to follow in my father's fatal footsteps. It wasn't until I flirted with suicide myself that I realized that something needed to change, or I was done.

When I was 17 years old (and in a whirlwind of denial and shame around my father's suicide) the opportunity for that change presented itself. I had the chance to travel from my home in California to Australia to visit family friends. On the surface, it was my dream trip. Even though I had only lived in Australia for a short time when I was younger, I felt a strong connection to the country.

While I was excited for the adventure, part of me was terrified. For the first two weeks of the trip I was scheduled to stay in Perth with our friends the Kennedys, who lived just a few blocks from where my dad had died. I knew I was going to have to face my dad's suicide; there was no avoiding it. Up until this point, I had done an incredible job of avoiding my father's suicide and had hardly spoken to anyone about it. While I was scared, a part of me was beginning to emerge that wanted to confront the past. I knew that I couldn't run away forever.

On my first day in Perth I had a life changing conversation with one of my father's closest friends, John David Kennedy (he and my father had grown up together in South Africa). We took a long walk along the beautiful Canning River near their house. During our walk, John David shared with me that his father had also died by suicide when he was a boy. A fact that I was unaware of prior to this trip.

He courageously opened up about some of the experiences and lessons which he had learned over the years from his father's suicide. For the first time since my father died I felt like I wasn't alone. When John David shared his experience with me it completely changed my perspective. Here was someone who had been through what I had and come out the other side. A strange thing happened after that, I felt like I not only could talk about my father's suicide, but that I wanted to. I opened up and spoke about my father's death with a sense of openness and freedom that I hadn't experienced before.

We took a rest on a wooden bench overlooking the river. I remember breathing more easily and deeply than I had in quite some time. It was as if I had been carrying around a backpack full of rocks and I was finally able to shed some of the weight. I remember being fully tuned in to the beauty of the present moment, to the sights, sounds, and scents all around me. It felt like I was back home in the ocean.

We sat taking in the scenery, and then John David turned to me and said, "You know, Sebastian, your dad was an incredible man. His death took such a toll on all of us who were close to him, especially you and your family. And while it was a great loss, I want you to know that this event in your past does not have to dictate your life. We all go through difficult times at one point or another. It can be so easy to use past difficulties as an excuse to make poor decisions in the present, to play the victim and blame life. Nothing that happened in the past has the power to control the decisions you make right now."

I listened intently as he went on to say, "I spent years running away from my father's death. I've learned that running away is not only ineffective, it's impossible. Until we turn to face what we're afraid of, it will always haunt us. If there is one thing I can pass along to you, it would be to stop running. And who knows? What you are seeking may just come to you."

I took a deep breath as I looked out over the flowing water. As I sat in the silence taking in what he shared, I saw that even more powerful than his words, John David was living proof of that realization. Here was someone who had gone through a very traumatic experience as a youth but didn't let that control or dictate his life. He had grown into a very grounded and successful person. This was my first glimmer of realizing that my past did not have total control over my life, that it did not control my destiny.

This conversation with John David allowed me to look at my father's death in a different light. I thought to myself, If the past can't control me, why do I have to fear it? And if I don't fear it, I can confront it and learn from it. That was the moment I began to look at my father's life and death as my teacher. I went from running away from my fears to turning and facing them.

It's amazing to think that one conversation can be enough to plant the seeds of change. For me it was the turning point in my process of stepping out from the shadows and into the light and eventually led to my book Ashes in the Ocean. I wrote Ashes in the Ocean because I wanted to offer to others what John David offered me. A space to have a conversation about a difficult topic and an invitation to face one's fears and start on a new path to a lighter and fuller future.

BUILDING YOUR MENTAL MECHANIC'S TOOLBOX

PART 3

TOOL #7: Adopting a Challenge Mindset

Mindsets are ideas and attitudes that shape the way you think about yourself and the world - it's your outlook on life. Much has been written about growth versus fixed mindsets in educational and sport psychology. Growth mindsets welcome challenges and new things and understand failure as an opportunity to learn. Fixed mindsets believe their intelligence and talent are fixed traits and that talent by itself - without effort - is responsible for success. People with fixed mindsets tend to avoid challenges because failure threatens their identity. Often the instructor in a martial arts class will advise all students from seasoned black belts to beginners to always come to class with the mindset of a white belt, a beginner, so you allow yourself the mental room to learn and grow. The story often told using the metaphor of a cup full of tea. If the cup is full of tea you cannot add anymore, and if your mind/brain is full it allows no room for new knowledge, Grasshopper.

When people are in crisis, stressors can feel like life-and-death threats - the cascading 'loss orientation' becomes overwhelming, and the negative inner voice gets very loud: "I can't!" "I quit!" "I'll never be able to!" "This is too hard!"

The challenge mindset is an intentional cognitive shift away from threat and loss mentality to one of growth and gain. We know that directing efforts toward positive, desirable goals yields much more success than avoiding negative stressors. In this exercise, see if you can identify your threat-oriented mindset and change it to a challenge-oriented one. See if you can embrace the challenge. If you are feeling revved-up shift from saying to yourself, "I am anxious about this threat" to, "I am excited about this challenge."

Many of us travel around the nation and world and often finds ourselves landing in foreign airports, not knowing a soul, and not knowing the local culture. We can think of this somewhat unsettling experience as an adventure, a once in a lifetime adventure, as we will never see the place again with new eyes.

Examples of my fixed and threat thinking:

Can you shift to:

- "I am challenged by and growing through these challenges."

- "I recognize and reward the fact that I am taking steps to transform myself through this opportunity."

- "I can't do it... yet."

- "I am trying new things to grow through this crisis."

Write out your own:

TOOL #8: Know Your Crisis Resources

Knowing your crisis resources BEFORE you are in crisis will make it easier to navigate the crisis later. Kick the tires on these by checking them out; if you or a family member or friend need them later, you will know where to turn:

- National Suicide Prevention Lifeline: 1-800-273-8255 http://suicide-preventionlifeline.org/

- Crisis Text Line: Text HELLO to 741741[30]

- Ask your employer if they have an Employee Assistance Program

- Reach out to someone you are close to who lives with mental illness. They are less likely to be judgmental, and chances are that they won't 'should' all over you. You know, "You should do this, and you should do that, and you should try fish oil."

EPILOGUE

Craig's Poem: What if?

I'm eight years old and I'm thinking about suicide. I'm thinking about life, about death about the maddening puzzle we are blindly left to piece together. I'm thinking how hard it is to go to school when I don't know if today will end in a passing grade or a bloody nose. I'm thinking about my only friend, a man three times my age who continually puts his hands on my skin in a way that I know is not supposed to happen. I'm thinking what if feels like to lay down at night and cover my head to hide from the fighting screams and the breaking glass that's coming from the other room in a place that I am forced to call my home.

But more than anything I'm thinking what if? What if I didn't live this life?

I'm fifteen years old and I'm thinking about suicide. I'm standing in a psychiatric hospital with long thin lines trailing across my arms, chest, and stomach... there is a man in front of me asking why? Why did you do this to yourself? I'm thinking I want to tell him, but I can't. I can't because I don't know. I'm thinking, maybe it's because I wanted someone to be able see what it feels like to be me. Maybe it's because I wanted the pain on this inside to show on the outside. Maybe it's because the thoughts in my mind have become so overrun with illness that pain has become my only reality. I'm thinking... Maybe it's because no one quite understands how bad it hurts to be me.

But more than anything I'm thinking what if? What if I didn't live this life?

I'm twenty years old and I'm thinking about suicide. I'm sitting on the edge of rented bed in a house that I have no business calling home. My mind is overrun with the painful memories of my entire lifetime. The days of being bullied when the only thing I learned from elementary school was how to run from balled up fists and angry, pointing fingers. I'm thinking about the years of growing up in a house that taught me home meant nothing more than slamming doors and deep slow breaths. I'm thinking about when I told her I loved her, and she couldn't say she loved me back. I'm thinking how I've spent more time in a psychiatric hospital than I ever have in classrooms.

But more than anything I'm thinking what if. What if I didn't live this life?

I'm thirty-four years old. I'm standing at an altar. There is a woman standing next to me that I can't even begin to describe to you. She is so powerful... and so beautiful. And she is saying yes. Yes, I will spend the rest of my life with you. I'm thinking how fortunate I am in this moment. I'm thinking how grateful I am to have once had my heart broken so badly that I can truly appreciate what it means to have it healed.

But more than anything, I'm thinking what if. What if I hadn't lived this life?

I'm thirty-five years old. I'm sitting on the edge of a bed that I own. In a house that I bought. In a place that I can truly call my home. In my arms is a baby girl with eyes so blue they actually dissolve my heart. I'm thinking what if. What if I hadn't lived this life? What if I hadn't spent so many nights hiding under my covers from the violence as a child, would I ever have the passion to create a home of my own built on a foundation of peace? I'm thinking, what if I never felt the hands of a man destroy my body and my mind before they even had the chance to be develop. Would I have ever been able to look into my daughter's eyes and say with this level of commitment that I will protect you?

My God, what if I hadn't lived this life?

I'm forty-one years old. I'm standing on a stage in front a room full of people, and there is a heart beating openly on my sleeve. And I'm thinking what if. What if I never lived this life? What if I had never learned to fight against the crushing grip of mental illness despite the countless times it tried to destroy me? Would I have ever had the courage to tell you this? What if I never learned to stand face-to-face with my deepest fears and say I will commit. I will commit to the rest of this life no matter how hard it gets, no matter how scared I am. Would I have ever known what it means to have bravery not only flow through my words but through my veins? I'm thinking what if... what if I hadn't spent so many nights believing in a God who taught me the only thing, I really needed to believe in was myself. What if I hadn't cried so many tears that I submerged myself in a pool of self-discovery?

I'm standing in front of you today and I'm thinking What if... What if I hadn't lived this life? And I can tell you, I'm so grateful I have.

Craig A. Miller

Author/Speaker

www.ThisisHowitFeels.com

http://www.suicidology.org/home

FAQ

How do I know when it's time to find professional help?

Your mental machine is not that different from your car, in a way. How do you know when it's time to go to a mechanic? When you have a light come on in your car that you don't recognize, you take out your manual and try to figure out what that light is. Sometimes it's an easy fix. Sometimes the manual gives you ideas of things you can try and, if you get lucky, problem solved! But sometimes you see the light come on, and you look in the manual and either it doesn't have the answer, or you try the suggestions and those don't help. It's time to call a friend or a mechanic. But keep in mind, if your engine is smoking you need to take immediate action!

How do I tell my family/friends that I am overwhelmed?

Telling our friends and family that we are struggling can be one of the hardest things to do, and for that reason, men often do not communicate clearly. They use vague statements like, "I am tired," or, "I am frustrated," which don't truly convey the experience you may be having. It's important to be as clear as you can be because friends and families often miss vague messages and that leaves people feeling like nobody's listening or no one cares, which is NOT the case!

Think of it this way, if you bring your car to a mechanic and you tell him or her that the check engine light is on but you don't tell him or her that you heard a loud crack, sparks flew and that you saw smoke, it's possible the mechanic will not be as thorough in trying to figure the problem out. The same thing can happen to our friends and family!

How do I help a family member or friend I am worried about?

If you are worried about someone, it's important to reach out to them. Tell them that you care about them and you have noticed that something seems different. Make sure you emphasize that you are there for them to talk to! That you want to be that person in their life they can lean on.

It's also important to get others involved. We never talk about people's mental health or other personal struggles as gossip so any communication we have about someone we are worried about should be with people we believe care about that person too, and we trust that they will be supportive. You should not worry about someone alone or feel solely responsible for their wellbeing.

How do I find the right help?

Finding the 'right' help can be challenge because sometimes we don't know what's wrong. Just like we need a diagnosis of a car problem, we need to know what is causing our problems. With a car the problem could be in the electrical system, so you take it to a shop that specializes in electrical issues. It could be a transmission problem, so you take it to a transmission shop. Men who participated in our surveys overwhelmingly reported that when they are struggling, they turn to their family and significant other first and then their friends. This is a good starting place but like any other problems, if you start off there and you don't get what you need, you know it's time to try the next step which could be talking to your primary care physician or seeking mental health care. Remember, they can't help you as well if you aren't totally honest with what is going on. If you don't mention to the mechanic at the transmission shop that you can only drive the car in reverse, he's going to waste a lot of time (and your money) figuring out the problem.

How do you start the process of finding a therapist or treatment center?

How do you find the right mechanic? You shop around. You do your research. Personal references are often helpful if you feel comfortable talking to the people in your life, but you can also ask your primary care physician for suggestions or search online.

Look for a provider that has experience in whatever it is you 'think' you're struggling with. If it turns out to be something other than you thought, they should be able to help you figure that out. If the person or program you get connected to doesn't seem like the right fit, try something else. You can advocate for what works best for you, just keep persisting (not avoiding).

What if people judge me? What if they discriminate against me?

Your mental health care is protected health information. It is possible that people may recognize that something seems off with you but that's more likely to happen because you didn't seek help than because you did. If people are judging you, maybe they are not the best people to surround yourself with. If you are discriminated against, the law is on your side.

How do I help others who have gone through something similar?

Think about the people that have helped you in your life. What was the best advice or support anyone gave you? Usually, it is just that they showed up and listened intently. Speak from your own experiences. What we find is often most helpful for people is knowing that they have someone they can turn to who isn't judging them and has been through similar experiences.

Also be aware of things people have said or done that were unhelpful. Sometimes we get frustrated with people we care about, and we let that frustration show, but rarely have people gotten better because they felt others were frustrated with them. The same thing is true for judgment.

How do I tell my story?

Take time to think through how you might tell your story before you start. One question to ask is, "Am I ready?" Are you solid enough in your wellness to go back into 'the dark forest?' Have you alerted your support system (including counselors and sponsors) that you are considering telling your story? What is your 'why?' Why do you want to tell your story? How might it be helpful to you and the others you will share it with? Think through what publicly telling your story might mean to your future self or other people in your story. Different people will have different perspectives on 'the truth,' so prepare yourself that not everyone will agree with your version.

Once you've worked through these questions, then dig into the well-known best practices for safe and effective storytelling. One great resource is Joseph Campbell's "A Hero's Journey" - an archetypal storytelling structure that helps you frame your narrative through a lens of redemption and transformation. If you are telling a story about suicide - loss, attempt or thoughts - be sure to consult best practices on safe messaging and preferred language. Don't glamorize or romanticize suicide or talk in detail about the means or other triggering details.

Once you have your story in a version that feels right for you and your take-away point to your audience is clear, practice telling your story in safe circles. Get feedback and see how it feels. Some people stop there, and that is okay. Having witnesses to your journey is all you may need. Others leverage their stories for systems and cultural change. That is also important.

Your story is your story. All stories matter.

Glossary

Airbags: A self-care plan to soften the blow in case of minor or major life event, that doesn't always seem necessary until you really need it.

Anthology: A collection of selected literary pieces or passages, or works of art or music

Anxiety: The term 'anxiety disorder' refers to specific psychiatric disorders that involve extreme fear or worry, and includes generalized anxiety disorder (GAD), panic disorder and panic attacks, agoraphobia, social anxiety disorder, selective mutism, separation anxiety, and specific phobias. Think of it as your car's engine running too fast, at length, for any one of many reasons; fuel is too rich, carburetor is misadjusted, gas pedal is sticking, etc.

Bipolar disorder: Bipolar disorder, also known as manic-depressive illness, is a brain disorder that causes unusual shifts in mood, energy, activity levels, and the ability to carry out day-to-day tasks. There are four basic types of bipolar disorder; all of them involve clear changes in mood, energy, and activity levels. Like an automatic transmission that slips from gear to gear, from 1st, to 2nd, to 3rd, to 4th, and back.

Confidentiality: The principle that within the medical and mental health fields, providers can not disclose your protected health information, including but not limited to that they see you as a client, what your diagnosis is or your treatment. Your auto mechanic can tell anyone they want that you hadn't changed the oil since you bought the car.

Crisis: With a car, it could be a variety of things that can go wrong, often quickly, like a tire blows out, brakes fail, power steering pump gives up, and a telephone pole that jumps into your path, totaling the car. Mentally, it could be a reaction to a traumatic event or over-whelming life circumstance. It would also be a significant depressive or manic episode, an overdose, or a severe panic attack.

Crisis Center: A physical location within the community that you or your loved ones can go to or call for guidance if your 'check engine' light is on. Like your local mechanic when your car exhibits the same behavior.

Crisis Hotline: A phone number that you can call 24 hours a day, seven days a week for roadside assistance or technical support. Like the phone number for AAA, or your brother-in-law who is a great shade tree mechanic.

Depression: Depression (major depressive disorder) is a common and serious medical illness that negatively affects how you feel, the way you think, and how you act. Fortunate-ly, it is also treatable. Depression causes feelings of sadness and often a loss of interest in activities once enjoyed. It can lead to a variety of emotional and physical problems and can decrease a person's ability to function at work and at home. Your tires are losing air to the point where the car won't move.

DIY: Do It Yourself, change your own oil, keep the tires properly inflated, fluids topped off, rotate the tires, replace the wipers and the air filter; in other words, a self-care plan.

Flares: Something to warn others as they approach that all is not well with you, and steer clear. Being up front with friends, family, and coworkers when you're struggling mentally, so they can pitch in and help you cope.

Gambling Addiction: You know the brakes need replacing; you've been hearing that telltale metal-on-metal sound for longer than you can remember, but you roll the dice, month after month, until they come up craps, and the results are catastrophic. You know you shouldn't be gambling, you refuse to admit, even to yourself, that you've got a gambling problem, and believe that you will show everyone when you get that big win, so you continue to roll the dice, until they come up craps, and you lose everything.

Gauges: Oil temperature, engine temperature, gasoline, tachometer; are you operating within safe parameters, do you have plenty of energy, and is your mind moving a normal speed, and your temper in the cool range and holding?

General maintenance: Oil change, fluids topped off, wiper blades, air filter, tire rotations, and paying attention to the warning lights on the dashboard; everyday self-care, diet, exercise, meditation, medication, and paying attention to signs that all may not be well and doing something about it.

Grief: The normal and natural emotional reaction to loss or change of any kind. Of itself, grief is neither a pathological condition nor a personality disorder. Grief can also be feelings caused by the end of or change in a familiar pattern of behavior.

Jumper cables: Activities, therapy, meds to get one jump-started when their personal batteries are drained, and accepting help from friends, family, loved ones, and the appropriate mental health professional. If your car battery dies, jumper cables cannot charge the battery, you're going to need someone else with a car to give you a jump.

Means: The tool or tools that are utilized to attempt to end one's life. (i.e. medication, guns, rope, razor blade, running car and a garden hose).

Means Restriction: Reducing one's access to lethal tools when at risk for self-harm.

Mechanic: Psychologist, psychiatrist, therapist, or another counselor. Like a professional, well-trained, and certified car mechanic or highly trained peer supporter or peer specialist.

Mental disorder: Problem with the smooth running of the brain due to any number causes. Like dirty fuel, clogged fuel injector, blocked catalytic converter, or generally out of tune.

Mental Fitness: Maintaining the brain (and the body attached) in tip top running shape. Like performing the scheduled maintenance and diagnosing and fixing unscheduled car problems quickly.

Mental health: Refers to our cognitive, behavioral, and emotional wellbeing - it is all about how we think, feel, and behave. The term 'mental health' is sometimes used to mean an absence of a mental disorder. Your car is operating within acceptable parameters for a mechanized, self-propelled vehicle.

Mental illness: See Mental Disorder

Overhaul: You cannot repair the engine, you must rebuild or replace it. Your current situation, whatever you're doing, is not maintaining your mental health and it cannot be fixed in its current state; changes must be made. Like changing jobs, where you live, to whom you are married or in a relationship with, your circle of friends, your mental and physical health habits, and your current medication regimen need to be changed or adjusted.

Positive Psychology: The scientific study of the strengths that enable individuals and communities to thrive. The field is founded on the belief that people want to lead meaningful and fulfilling lives, to cultivate what is best within themselves, and to enhance their experiences of love, work, and play.

Prevention: The action of stopping something from happening or arising. Regular, scheduled maintenance for your car.

Protective Factors: Conditions or attributes (skills, strengths, resources, supports, or coping strategies) in individuals, families, communities, or the larger society that help people deal more effectively with stressful events and mitigate or eliminate risk in families and communities. Think of the undercoating you apply to the underside of a car to prevent corrosion and rust.

Resilience: The process of adapting well in the face of adversity, trauma, tragedy, threats, or significant sources of stress - such as family and relationship problems, serious health problems or workplace and financial stressors. It means "bouncing back" from difficult experiences. Like using a high mileage detergent motor oil to give extra protection to an older engine.

Risk Factors: Characteristics at the biological, psychological, family, community, or cultural level that precede and are associated with a higher likelihood of negative outcomes. For your car it can be foul weather, rough roads or terrain, excessive temperatures, etc.

Screenings: A mental health screening is the process of gathering information to help a person assess quickly whether or not symptoms need more attention. Hooking your car up to the mechanic's computer and interpreting from the codes displayed what is wrong with the vehicle.

Self-care: Means choosing behaviors that balance the effects of emotional and physical stressors: exercising, eating healthy foods, getting enough sleep, practicing yoga or meditation or relaxation techniques, abstaining from substance abuse, pursuing creative outlets, engaging in psychotherapy. Choosing to do regular and scheduled maintenance on your vehicle.

Self-harm: Is the deliberate infliction of damage to your own body and includes cutting, burning, and other forms of injury. While cutting can look like attempted suicide, it's often not; most people who mutilate themselves do it to regulate mood. People who hurt themselves in this way may be motivated by a need to distract themselves from inner turmoil or to quickly release anxiety that builds due to an inability to express intense emotions. Purposely driving your vehicle 'into the ground.'

Snow Tires & Chains: Safety equipment, often required, to travel roads slick with ice and snow. Being prepared, ahead of time, for mental health crises.

Social Supports: Refers to the various types of support (i.e., assistance/help) that people receive from others and is generally classified into three major categories: emotional (e.g., providing empathy), instrumental (e.g., providing practical assistance), and informational (e.g., providing resources) support. When it comes to your vehicle, think AAA.

Stigma: Refers to the disapproval and shame felt by people exhibiting characteristics that society considers wrong or unusual. These characteristics may be related to racial or cultural identity, sexual identity, social status, physical appearance, disease or disability, or other personal traits. In the world of cars, people see the outside of you and make judgments to drive around you based on the make of your car.

Substance Abuse: A maladaptive pattern of substance use leading to clinically significant impairment or distress, as manifested by one (or more) of the following, occurring within a 12-month period. Recurrent substance use resulting in a failure to fulfill major role obligations at work, school, or home (e.g., repeated absences or poor work performance related to substance use; substance-related absences, suspensions, or expulsions from school; neglect of children or household). Using low octane fuel, in a vehicle requiring high octane, over a long period of time, eventually affecting performance.

Suicide: Taking one's own life voluntarily and intentionally.

Suicide Attempt Survivors: People on a continuum of suicidal experience, from those who have seriously contemplated suicide and had a near miss to those who have attempted and lived through their experience.

Suicide Loss Survivors: Someone who has lost a friend, family member, or loved one to suicide.

Tempered glass: Things that minimize damage in case of a bad episode (peer support group, sponsor, etc.). Also known as safety glass, tempered glass breaks down into smaller pieces that have fewer sharp edges. This is possible because during the annealing process the glass is cooled down slowly, which makes the glass much stronger and scratch resistant compared to non-treated glass.

Troubleshooting: Is the term used for thinking or thought processes that are specifically aimed at finding solutions to specific mental health problems. With your car, it can be anything from a test-drive to listening to it run to connecting it to a diagnostic computer.

Tune-up: On many of the newer cars, spark plugs, fuel, and air filters and PCV valve retain some of the items that we consider part of a 'tune-up.' Because the phrase 'tune-up' can mean so many different things, the manufactures don't list tune-ups in their maintenance schedules. Mentally, it can be something as simple as a proper diet, exercise, and good night's sleep, and as complex as a combination of therapy, medication, meditation, and in severe cases, hospitalization.

MEET THE MECHANICS

Ethan Fisher is a preventive and motivational keynote speaker. Drawing from his own experience as a promising high school basketball star whose struggle with addiction culminated in a life-altering tragedy, Ethan travels to campuses all over the country, educating students about the risks of underage drinking, substance abuse, negative peer pressure, and untreated depression. Ethan holds two bachelor's degrees and an MBA earned while coaching men's college basketball. In 2012, Ethan founded his non-profit venture Life CONsequences as a platform to bring his message to middle and high school students. He started UnDrafted in 2014, a small LLC tailored to reaching student athletes through their college athletic programs.

Dr. Jeremy Fletcher is currently an Assistant Professor at the University of South Alabama's Doctor of Physical Therapy program in Mobile, AL. His experiences with grief, PTSD, and anxiety extend beyond his personal experiences and into his clinical practice, research, and consulting with Veterans Recovery Resources, a non-profit whose mission is to reduce barriers to mental wellness for Veterans struggling with substance abuse and other comorbid conditions. His work in psychologically informed physical therapy practice and health promotion led to his recent naming as a Robert Wood Johnson Foundation Clinical Scholar Fellow, a program designed to empower leaders to transform our society into a Culture of Health. Jeremy can be reached at jfletcher@southalabama.edu.

Doug Gertner, Ph.D., is an educator, trainer, broadcast-
er, and activist whose professional career includes service
to higher education, corporate, organizational, men's issues,
and fatherhood consulting. He has taught at ten colleges and
universities in Colorado and Wyoming, lectured, published, and
consulted widely in the areas of education, management, and
gender studies. Since 2000, Doug has worked independently

to deliver training, team building, and facilitation for a list of premiere clients as principal of
Doug Gertner Workplace Seminars and Solutions. Doug's alter-ego, The Grateful Dad, brings
a laid-back, rock-n-roll wisdom to fatherhood topics. Doug and his partner Maggie Miller are
parents of a college-age son, Jordan.

John Lally is a retired psychiatric nurse practitioner with a
master's degree in nursing and in Marriage and Family Therapy
and has worked in the field of psychiatry and substance abuse
for the last 34 years. Since the death of his son Timothy, John
has organized and is the Executive Director of Today I Matter,
Inc. whose mission is to work to reduce the shame and stigma
of mental illness and addiction while promoting the physical,

emotional, and mental health of our communities. Through John's public speaking he tells
the story of his family and his son Tim's struggle with substance use and mental illness. John
lives in Connecticut with his wife and remains close with his surviving son.

DeQuincy Lezine is a suicide attempt survivor who has been active in suicide prevention since 1996. He received his Ph.D. in Clinical Psychology from UCLA. and completed a postdoctoral fellowship at the University of Rochester. Dr. Lezine is the Chair of the Attempt Survivor and Lived Experience Division of AAS and Co-Chair of the Consumer Survivor Committee for the National Suicide Prevention Lifeline. Dr. Lezine was awarded the Lifetime Achievement Award at the SAMHSA 2015 Voice Awards. He is CEO of Prevention Communities, Director of the Lived Experience Academy, and author of Eight Stories Up.

Govan A. Martin, III, retired as a 29-year veteran of the Pennsylvania State Police (PSP) (1983-2012). In his tenure in the PSP, Govan worked in patrol, crime, and the highlight of his career was becoming Manager of the Member Assistance Program. Govan started the Annual Law Enforcement Employee Assistance/Peer Support Program Conference in 2006 for State Police agencies across the country, along with the FBI, to build a cooperative network among Law Enforcement EAP agencies to better assist personnel from their respective Departments. Govan has been a keynote speaker for Employee Assistance/ Peer Support Programs, CISM conferences across the country. Currently Govan is the Chair of the Board of Directors for Prevent Suicide PA. He is also doing private consulting for various organizations for suicide prevention and critical/traumatic incident training.

Craig Miller is an author, speaker, and suicide attempt survivor. For years he struggled with OCD, extreme anxiety, depression, and suicidal thoughts. After a suicide attempt at age 20, Craig became dedicated to understanding what led him to such a decision and, more importantly, how he could gain control of himself and his life to ensure it would never happen again. He published his first book in 2012 titled *This is How it Feels: a memoir of attempting suicide and finding life.* Craig

and his story have been featured in the Boston Globe as well as several other media outlets including the documentary *A Voice At The Table* and the full-length film *The S Word*.

Joel Phillips is an active stay-at-home father. He and his wife make their home in Lakewood, Colorado. They are first time parents to an amazing baby boy (born September 2016). Joel embraces managing the household and volunteers in the community. His passion is to see that people live a fulfilled, enriching life, and he also coaches participants in Landmark Worldwide's Self Expression and Leadership Program,

which is designed to empower participants to live a life they love. Choosing life in his darkest moment meant living a life even he couldn't dream and contributing to this book is what he describes as one of his greatest life experiences.

Mike Schnittgen has found a new career, recently accepting a position as a school counselor in his home state. He continues to learn how to help others with their crises and is currently adding to his education by enrolling in courses leading to certification as a licensed addictions counselor. He is thankful every day that being a father saved his life and always makes time for his beautiful little fishing buddy. Mike hopes to help raise awareness and improve mental standards in the rail industry to reduce and eliminate the mental health struggles of the underappreciated members of the rail industry.

As a young boy, Sebastian Slovin lost his father to suicide, which would deeply inspire his path in life. Later, he had the opportunity to travel extensively as a professional bodyboarder. He holds a BA in Environmental Policy from San Diego State University and an MA in Leadership Studies from the University of San Diego. Sebastian's recent memoir, *Ashes in the Ocean*, is about living through and learning from his father's suicide. Since releasing his book Sebastian has been sharing his story to a wide range of audiences. He has also been featured on a variety of media including National Public Radio, Fox 5 News, the San Diego Union Tribune, and numerous podcasts.

Greg van Borssum is a failed schoolkid who turned adversities into opportunities, from martial arts to movies. Over the years Greg has accomplished an incredible level of achievement, the world's youngest professional natural bodybuilder, a multiple black belt martial artist, and award-winning Hollywood film maker. But the successes aren't what made him.

It was forging his pathway to those achievements that taught Greg the value of the true Warrior's Code. Time after time he drew on that warrior mindset to battle through failures and losses, which included overcoming the pain of losing twelve people from his life to depression and suicide. His mindset gave him the resilience to turn his setbacks into comebacks that have made him the mentor and speaker he is today.

Rourke Weaver has been in recovery since April 12, 2007. He is the Director of Business Development with Red Rock Recovery Center (RRRC), an extended care program in Lakewood, Colorado focused on bringing a long-term, high quality and balanced approach of Peer and Clinical services. In Rourke's free time he still enjoys an active lifestyle, maintaining a close relationship with his family (both of blood and choice) and

proudly acknowledging being a nerd... loving D&D, video games and all things Sci-Fi & Fantasy. Rourke would also like to acknowledge Sarah, his partner of 5 years, who has become his major source of strength, support, and inspiration.

Endnotes

1   Conejero, I., Olié, E., Courtet, P., & Calati, R. (2018). Suicide in older adults: current perspectives. Clinical interventions in aging, 13, 691–699. doi:10.2147/CIA.S130670

2   Case, A. & Deaton, A. (2017). Mortality and morbidity in the 21st century. Retrieved on November 20, 2017 from https://www.brookings.edu/wp-content/uploads/2017/03/6_casedeaton.pdf.
Boddy, J. (2017, March 23). The Forces Driving Middle-Aged White People's 'Deaths Of Despair'. NPR. Retrieved on November 20, 2017 from https://www.npr.org/sections/health-shots/2017/03/23/521083335/the-forces-driving-middle-aged-white-peoples-deaths-of-despair.

3   Katz, Jackson (1995a). Reconstructing masculinity in the locker room: The Mentors in Violence Prevention Project. Harvard Educational Review, Vol. 65, No. 2, Summer.

Katz, Jackson (1995b). Advertising and the construction of violent white masculinity. In G. Dines & J. Humez (Eds.), Gender, race and class in media: A text reader. Thousand Oaks, CA: Sage Publications.

4   Spencer-Thomas, S., Quinnett, P. & Hindman, J. (2013, April 26). Man Therapy: An Innovative Approach to Suicide Prevention among Working Aged Men. Keynote, American Association of Suicidology conference in Austin, Texas.

5   Joiner, T. (2011). Lonely at the Top: The High Cost of Men's Success. New York City: St. Martin's Press.

6   Murthy, V. (2017, September). Work and the loneliness epidemic. Harvard Business Review. Retrieved on June 4, 2018 from https://hbr.org/cover-story/2017/09/work-and-the-loneliness-epidemic

7   Gilbert, B. & Bedi, R. (2014, October). Be a Man! Male Identity, Social Change in Contemporary America, and the Impact on Mental Health. Presentation at the Washington State Psychological Association Conference. Retrieved on June 3, 2018 from https://c.ymcdn.com/sites/www.wapsych.org/resource/resmgr/Fall_Convention_Handouts/Be_a_Man-FC_2014_Handout.pdf.

8   Kramer, K. Z., Kelly, E. L., & McCulloch, J. B. (2013). Stay-at-home fathers. Definition and characteristics based on 34 years of CPS data. Journal of Family Issues, doi: 10.1177/0192513X13502479

9   Harrington, B., Van Duesen, F., Fraone, J. S., Eddy, S., Haas., L. (2014). The new dad: take your leave. Perspectives on paternity leave from fathers, leading organizations, and global policies. Boston College Center for Work & Family.

10 Felmlee, D., Sweet, E., Sinclair, H. C. (2012). Gender rules: same- and cross-gender friendships norms. Sex Roles, Online. DOI 10.1007/s11199-011-0109-z

11 Heasley, R. (2004). Crossing the borders of gendered sexuality: Queer masculinities

of straight men. In C. Ingraham, (Ed.). Thinking Straight: The Promise, the Power, and the Paradox of Heterosexuality. New York: Routledge.

Henig, R. (2017). How Science Is Helping Us Understand Gender. National Geographic. Retrieved on June 3, 2018 from https://www.nationalgeographic.com/magazine/2017/01/how-science-helps-us-understand-gender-identity/.

12 Desjardins, B. (2004). Why is life expectancy longer for women than it is for men? Scientific American. Retrieved on June 3, 2018 from https://www.scientificamerican.com/article/why-is-life-expectancy-lo/?print=true.

13 Nam, S., Chu, H., Lee, M., Lee, J., Kim, N., & Lee S. (2010). A meta-analysis of gender differences in attitudes toward seeking professional psychological help. Journal of American College Health, 59(2):110-6. doi: 10.1080/07448481.2010.483714.

14 Joiner, T. (2007). Why People Die by Suicide. Cambridge, MA: Harvard University Press.

15 Pirkis, J., Spittal, M., Keogh, L., Mousaferiadis, T. & Currier, D. (2017). Masculinity and suicidal thinking. Social Psychiatry and Psychiatric Epidemiology, 52(3), 319–327.

16 Spencer-Thomas, S., Quinnett, P. & Hindman, J. (2013, April 26). Man Therapy: An Innovative Approach to Suicide Prevention among Working Aged Men. Keynote, American Association of Suicidology conference in Austin, Texas.

17 National Institute of Mental Health (n.d.) Men and depression. Retrieved on June 4, 2018 from https://www.nimh.nih.gov/health/publications/men-and-depression/index.shtml.

18 Wang, H. & Liu, Y. (2003). Association between social support and health outcomes: A meta-analysis. The Kaohsiung Journey of Medical Sciences, 19(7): 345-350.

19 Now Matters Now (n.d.) Paced breathing. Retrieved on July 6, 2018 from https://www.nowmattersnow.org/skill/paced-breathing

20 Edenfield, T. & Saeed, S. (2012). An update on mindfulness meditation as a self-help treatment for anxiety and depression. Psychology Research and Behavior Management. 5:131–141. Retrieved on July 6, 2018 from https://www.ncbi.nlm.nih.gov/pmc/articles/PMC3500142/.

21 Cascio, C., O'Donnell, M., Tinney, F., Lieberman, M., Taylor, S., Strecher, V. & Falk, E. (2016). Self-affirmation activates brain systems associated with self-related processing and reward and is reinforced by future orientation. Social Cognitive and Affective Neuroscience, 11 (4), 621–629. Retrieved on July 6, 2018 from https://academic.oup.com/scan/article/11/4/621/2375054

22 Ibid

23 WikiHow (n.d.) How to Write and Effective Affirmation. Retrieved on July 7, 2018 from https://www.wikihow.com/Write-an-Effective-Affirmation.

24 Dresdale, R. (2016). Work-Life Balance Vs. Work-Life Integration, Is There Really A Difference? Forbes. Retrieved on July 7, 2018 from https://www.forbes.com/sites/rachelritlop/2016/12/18/work-life-balance-vs-work-life-integration-is-there-really-a-difference/#4788b7763727

25 Pearson, T. (n.d.). The Best Morning Routine (Backed by Science). Retrieved on July 7, 2018 from https://taylorpearson.me/morning/.

26 Defense Centers of Excellence (2011). Best Practices Identified for Peer Support Programs. Retrieved on December 11, 2017 from https://gacc.nifc.gov/cism/documents/Best_Practices_Identified_for_Peer_Support_Programs.pdf.

27 Intentional Peer Support https://www.intentionalpeersupport.org/

28 Next Level Leadership Coaching (n.d.). What is Leadership Coaching? Retrieved on December 11, 2017 from http://www.nextlevelleadershipcoaching.com/what-is-leader-ship-coaching/.

29 Taylor, J. (2012). Crisis: Emotional threat or challenge? Psychology Today. Retrieved on January 19, 2018 from https://www.psychologytoday.com/blog/the-power-prime/201203/crisis-emotional-threat-or-challenge.

30 Text HELLO to 686868 for Canada and 85258 for the UK

Made in the USA
Monee, IL
01 February 2022

90418933R00103